QGIS MAP DESIGN

ANITA GRASER

GRETCHEN N. PETERSON

loca+e
PRESS

Credits & Copyright

QGIS Map Design

by Anita Graser and Gretchen N. Peterson

Published by Locate Press LLC

Direct permission requests to info@locatepress.com or mail:
Locate Press LLC, PO Box 671897, Chugiak, AK, USA, 99567-1897

Editor   Gary Sherman
Cover Design   Julie Springer
Interior Design   Based on Memoir-LATEXdocument class
Publisher Website   http://locatepress.com
Book Website   http://locatepress.com/qmd

Contents

Foreword

QGIS has come a long way in its fourteen years of life. From humble beginnings as a mere data viewer, it now provides a vast array of GIS functionality, tool integration, extensible plugins, and—cartographic capability.

Slighted in years past for its inability to make a "pretty" map, QGIS now boasts a hefty complement of features that move it to the forefront. In this book, Anita and Gretchen have put together an impressive set of recipes that will help you not only learn new techniques, but really bump up the quality of your maps.

The recipes in the book are tailored for use with the QGIS Long Term Release (LTR), version 2.14. You'll also need a basic familiarity with QGIS, as the authors jump right in to the cartographic waters.

I know you'll learn a lot from the techniques presented within, and be able to adapt and evolve them to get the most out of your mapping projects.

I hope you enjoy the book!

GARY SHERMAN

Founder of QGIS / Publisher at Locate Press LLC

1. Introduction

1.1 Introduction

It's an exciting time to be a QGIS user. Over the last few years, QGIS has become a feature-rich Geographic Information System (GIS) application with an excellent suite of cartographic tools supporting the creation of all kinds of modern map styles, your imagination being the only limit. Every software update seems to bring at least a few new whiz-bang cartographic capabilities that expand the possibilities even further, and with the advent of the Long Term Release (LTR) plan—a version kept up to date with bug fixes for at least a year—more organizations are beginning to incorporate QGIS into daily workflows.

In this book we demonstrate QGIS cartographic capabilities to aspiring and current GIS professionals, provide reference material for great map designs, and serve as a source of mapping inspiration.

A free and open-source software project, QGIS relies on, and benefits from, the varied community that supports it. As such, we encourage you to not only learn QGIS, but to get involved as well. There are many ways to help, including reporting bugs, participating in support forums, working on documentation, developing, and sponsoring. See the *Get Involved* page on the QGIS website[1] for more information.

The Authors

Anita Graser is a long-time QGIS community and project steering committee (PSC) member who is well known for a blog[2] that explains and illustrates many of the newest QGIS features and plugins as they are released. She is the author of *Learning QGIS*[3] and co-author of the *QGIS 2 Cookbook.*[4] Graser works at the Austrian Institute of Technology and frequently speaks on open source technology topics.

Gretchen Peterson publishes a blog[5] and is the author of *GIS Cartography: A Guide to Effective Map Design, Second Edition*[6] and *Cartographer's Toolkit: Colors, Typography, Patterns,*[7] all of which focus on teaching cartographic techniques. Peterson frequently speaks on cartography and runs the GIS consulting firm PetersonGIS.

By combining our skills, our goal was to create a book that would teach QGIS map design, cover much of the breadth of QGIS cartographic functionality, and do it with the most up-to-date map styling possible. The result is this book, and we hope that it opens you up to new possibilities in mapping and inspires you to show off your data with clarity and modernity.

Who This Book Is For

The primary audience we had in mind when writing this book is existing QGIS users who are familiar with the basics of working with spatial data, but who don't necessarily have a lot of—or any—experience with the cartographic tools, including layer styling methods, labeling techniques, or print map design.

We also see this book as a good introduction to QGIS for GIS professionals who are experienced with other GIS software and map designers who are looking for inspiration and are eager to explore the behind-the-scenes making of some of most avant-garde cartographic techniques today. The book focuses on static map design rather than webmap development, though many of the styling and labeling techniques can be applied to webmap design as well.

1. https://www.qgis.org/en/site/getinvolved/
2. http://anitagraser.com
3. http://loc8.cc/qmd/learning_qgis
4. http://loc8.cc/qmd/qgis_cookbook
5. http://www.gretchenpeterson.com/blog/
6. http://loc8.cc/qmd/gis_cartography
7. http://loc8.cc/qmd/cartographers_toolkit

How The Book Is Organized

This book is comprised of recipes of map designs and accompanying instructional texts. The recipes are ordered within each of the three main parts from easy, medium, difficult, to somewhat insane. These difficulty levels also largely correspond to the length of time needed to complete each recipe, which is indicated by the recipe's time wheel at the top of the page. The three main chapters are also progressive, starting with layer styling, moving to labeling, and finally print map design.

In some cases, recipes build on each other, such as in the case of Graduated Symbol Sizes, on page 19, which leads into the Restricted Labeling Using Expressions recipe, on page 97, which is further adapted in the Customizing Legends, on page 147 recipe. In these instances, the recipes indicate the progression and can be begun from scratch or started from the supplied project file.

For the most part, once a concept has been introduced (e.g., how to place halos around labels), the specific steps needed to produce that effect will not be repeated. This means that not every single step needed to complete the recipes is spelled out in detail, especially in the longer recipes near the end of the chapters, if the concept has been covered in a previous recipe. For example, the procedure to change the projection is detailed in the first recipe, Graduated Symbol Sizes, on page 19. Subsequent recipes indicate when a change in projection is needed along with the correct projection parameters but don't detail the procedure.

The beginning QGIS user may find it easier to begin with the simpler recipes and work through the book in order. Furthermore, more advanced QGIS users will appreciate getting to the substance of the design rather than wading through the technical minutiae in the later recipes.

Further Learning

The QGIS Training Manual[8] and the QGIS User Manual[9] provide much of the information needed to get started with QGIS and to look up specific functionality. Besides these online resources, there are multiple books on different QGIS topics listed on the project website.[10]

The QGIS API Documentation[11] and the QGIS PyQGIS Cookbook[12] are the definitive sites for developer resources. GIS StackExchange[13] is also a great place to post QGIS questions and search for answers.

Acknowledgements

We would like to thank Jonah Adkins and Brian Timoney for early map design critique and Matt Pettis for his help in locating U.S. election data. We would also like to thank the peer reviewers: Katherine Hurley, Sara Safavi, Nyall Dawson, and Johannes Kröger. We are indebted to the Natural Earth project, led by Nathaniel Kelso and Tom Patterson, for the bulk of the data used in the book's map designs. Finally, the authors wish to thank our tireless editor and publisher Gary Sherman, the founder of QGIS and owner of Locate Press.

---

8. http://loc8.cc/qmd/qgis_training_manual
9. http://loc8.cc/qmd/user_manual
10. http://loc8.cc/qmd/qgis_books
11. http://qgis.org/api/
12. http://loc8.cc/qmd/dev_cookbook
13. http://gis.stackexchange.com/

2. Getting Started

2.1 Getting Started

To get started, you'll need QGIS 2.14 Long Term Release (LTR) installed, as well as the files packaged in the QGIS Map Design Resources download.[14]

When you unzip the download, you'll find the QGIS project files for each recipe in the *projects* folder, data in the *geodata* folder, and the images and resources you'll need in their respective folders.

```
▼ 📁 qgis_map_design
   ▶ 📁 geodata
   ▶ 📁 images
   ▶ 📁 projects
   ▶ 📁 resources
```

With QGIS 2.4 and these files, you'll be ready dive right into the recipes. You can start each recipe from scratch with an empty QGIS project file (recommended) or you can skip ahead to the finished product by opening the recipe's QGIS project file. The project file already has all the data loaded and styled as described in the recipe, and other necessary components configured—such as completed Print Composers in the case of the Print Composer recipes.

The Data

The data used in the recipes comes primarily from Natural Earth , a public domain data collection of cultural and physical GIS data covering the globe at varying scales. The specific datasets used are found in the data folder, but there are many other datasets (and possibly updates to the data used in this book) that can be found by perusing the Natural Earth Download page.[15]

Map designs in this book that encompass more of a regional scale generally use data from OpenStreetMap in the Seattle, Washington area, supplied as a pre-processed SpatiaLite file. Seattle was chosen for its relatively good building cov-

erage, location along the coast, and interesting terrain. The OpenStreetMap data is available under the Open Database License, copyright OpenStreetMap contributors.

The terrain data for these regional recipes is a United States Geological Survey Digital Elevation Model from the University of Washington. A few other datasets from authoritative sources are also included to round out the designs.

They are, along with their respective originating locations:

```
Minnesota presidential election results, 2012:
    http://www.gis.leg.mn/html/election2012.html and
    http://electionresults.sos.state.mn.us/ENR/Home
Floodplains (fldplain_500yr):
    http://www5.kingcounty.gov/sdc/
Seattle neighborhoods (neighborhood):
    http://www5.kingcounty.gov/sdc/
Seattle water areas (wtrbdy):
    http://www5.kingcounty.gov/sdc/
```

All other datasets in the geodata folder will be created by you while working through the recipes or were created in advance by the authors to facilitate the designs. These are:

```
global_connected_cities
global_connections
global_countries_clipped
global_disk
highlight_service_area
highlight_utah
PathLength
seattle_bbox
seattle_contours
seattle_contours_tanaka
seattle_hillshade
```

Level of Effort

With all cartography projects, the process of finding spatial data tends to take up a large

---

14. http://locatepress.com/qgis_map_design_resources

15. http://www.naturalearthdata.com/downloads/

amount of the project time. We hope that the variety of datasets included in the resources for the book helps to lessen your QGIS cartography learning time considerably, while also providing you with several scales to work with, from neighborhood level data to global.

We've estimated the time to complete these recipes—it's shown in the time wheel found at the beginning of each recipe. Obviously the time to completion will depend on your prior familiarity with QGIS. These time estimates assume the you have a basic understanding of QGIS and will be working through each recipe from scratch, following along with the instructions.

Green (one slice) indicates that the recipe may take approximately thirty minutes to complete, yellow (two slices) is one hour, orange (three slices) is one and a half hours, and red (four slices) is two hours.

Part 1

Layer Styling

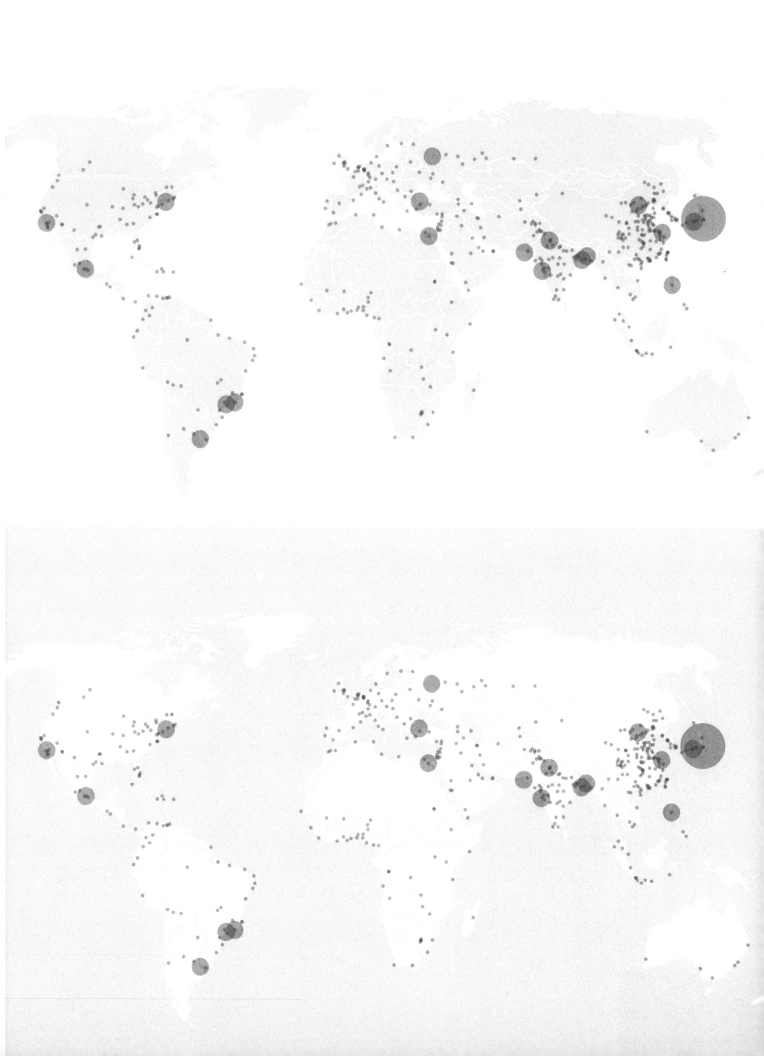

1. Graduated Symbol Sizes

This recipe illustrates how to create a newspaper style thematic map of the most populous metropolitan areas in the world. The metro areas are symbolized with semi-transparent circles that vary in size according to the population. The transparency allows circles to overlap and still be visible.

Varying the size of point features in accordance with their values as we do here is a common technique for highlighting proportional differences in magnitude. Usually this means circles or squares with different sizes for up to three to five value categories (e.g., low, medium, high). Less commonly, we see this technique used for line features where the thickness of line varies according to a value. In this recipe we use point data of cities, with larger circles to represent larger populations.

> To reproduce this map in QGIS, open the graduated_symbol_sizes.qgs project. The map in this recipe is also used in the Restricted Labeling and Customized Legend recipes.

1.1 Setting up the Map

We'll use the country shapefile:

```
ne_10m_admin_0_countries.shp
```

for the background and the population shapefile:

```
ne_10m_populated_places.shp
```

for the population points and values.

The metropolitan area population is specified in the field POP_MAX, which is the field we'll use, whereas the corresponding incorporated city population is specified in the field POP_MIN, which we won't use for this exercise.

Open the Layer Properties for the countries layer either by double-clicking the country layer in

the Layers Panel or by right-clicking the country layer and clicking on Properties. In the Style section of the dialog, change the color of the countries via the Simple fill, Colors, Fill, Choose color... drop-down option. Put in 230 for each of the R, G, and B values. Similarly, change the Border color to white, which can normally be found in the Standard colors section of the drop-down menu (unless the standard colors have previously been modified). The project will appear as shown in Figure 1.1.

There are many ways to specify colors in QGIS. In this recipe we use RGB color specifications since many people migrating to QGIS from other GIS software platforms will be familiar with the RGB system. In many other recipes in the book we specify colors in hex notation (e.g., #e6e6e6).

Figure 1.1: Countries symbolized with gray fill and white borders

Make sure the populated places layer is above the countries layer in the Layers Panel and open its Layer Properties dialog. Change the first drop-down in the Style section to Graduated and then put the following into the Column box:

```
POP_MAX / 1000000
```

This is shown in Figure 1.2.

Figure 1.2: Graduated symbols classified by the population column in millions

It's possible to simply type the expression into the box or, alternatively, use the expression button to the side of the box in order to open the Expression dialog. By doing this we get rid of the trailing zeros to condense the legend. You may have to click Apply to see this. Instead of the first category ending at 10,000,000.00, as it would if only POP_MAX were specified, it ends at 10.00000000. Remember that the numbers now denote the metropolitan populations in millions. Stay in the Layer Properties window for the next steps.

In the Symbol changer, change the color to RGB: 131 99 236, click OK, then use the transparency slider to change the transparency to 50%. Note that in this case we are setting the overall transparency of the symbols to 50%, which means that the circle borders and the fill color will be transparent. If we had instead changed the color opacity in the color selector then only the fill color would have been transparent.

Check the box next to Trim and change the Method to Size. In the Classes tab, change to Mode, Pretty Breaks. Notice that there are several classification methods available in the drop-down. We're choosing the Pretty Breaks classification for this visualization because it is a newer classification method that can be very useful. Put succinctly, a pretty breaks classification creates equally-spaced ranges with minimum and maximum values that are 1, 2, or 5 times a power of 10. For this map, keep the number of classes to the default of 5.

For reference, the classification options are:

- Pretty Breaks: equally-spaced ranges with minimum and maximum values that are 1, 2, or 5 times a power of 10; not particularly good for skewed data.

- Equal Interval: equal data value ranges; best for comparisons across time or between different datasets; not particularly good for skewed data.

- Quantile: equal number of data values in each category; best for comparisons across time or between different datasets; not particularly good for skewed data.

- Natural Breaks: minimum variation within categories, maximum variation between

categories; good for most data including skewed data; not particularly good for comparisons across time or between different datasets.

- Standard Deviation: categories for intervals above and below the mean; best for data with normal distributions; not particularly good for skewed data.

Notice that the first category in the resulting classification contains negative values and 0. To exclude these from the visualization, click the item in the list and then click Delete. Note that you could also uncheck that item in the list, which is helpful if there's a possibility that you'll want to show those values again in future design iterations. Take a moment to explore the additional options in each of the columns (i.e., Symbol, Values, Legend) by double-clicking them. For example, the values can be changed manually in the first category so that they span from 1 to 10, instead of 0 to 10, as shown in Figure 1.3. Go ahead and change the lowest value to 1.

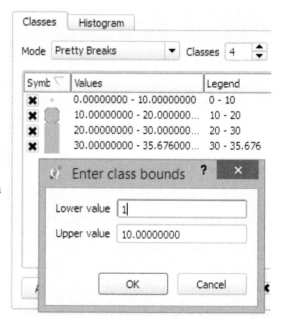

Figure 1.3: Class bounds

Now, double-click the first category in the list again (the one with values from 1 to 10), except double-click in the Symbol column. The Symbol selector appears. Change the Outline style to No Pen as shown in Figure 1.4, on the next page. Since it is the most numerous category, and this is a simple newspaper-style map, removing the border line from these symbols, while retaining the border on the larger symbols, helps to keep the map clean.

While still in the Symbol selector for that category, change the Size to 1. This also serves to de-emphasize the category. Click OK. The Layer Properties window should now appear as shown in Figure 1.5, on the following page.

Click OK to apply these changes to the map.

1.2 Changing the Projection

The spatial reference system for this QGIS project is EPSG:4326 - WGS 84, which is QGIS's global default coordinate reference system (unless you've customized this setting previously in Options). Because the map depicts relative sizes of metropolitan areas based on population, it would be better to change the projection to something that preserves area better. To this end, we'll change the projection of the map to World Robinson.

First, make sure that the layer `ne_10m_populated_places` has its Simplify Geometry property unchecked in the Layer Properties, Rendering window. We deactivate simplification because the combination with this dataset and the desired projection produces undesired results. Then, in the Project, Project Properties, CRS window, check the Enable 'on the fly' CRS transformation property and use the Filter to find the World Robinson projection, or alternatively, search by `EPSG:54030`. Once this is set the map should appear as shown in Figure 1.6, on page 23.

The global maps in this book all use the World Robinson projection unless otherwise noted.

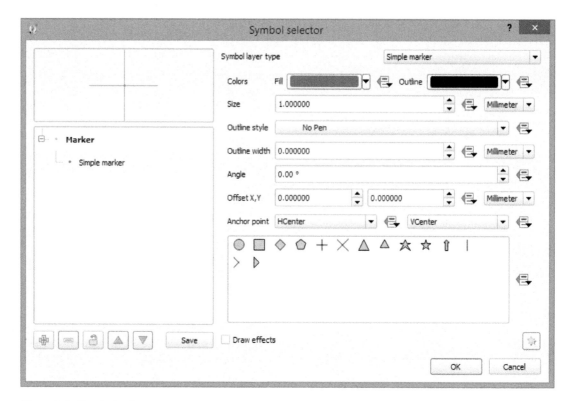

Figure 1.4: Symbol selector

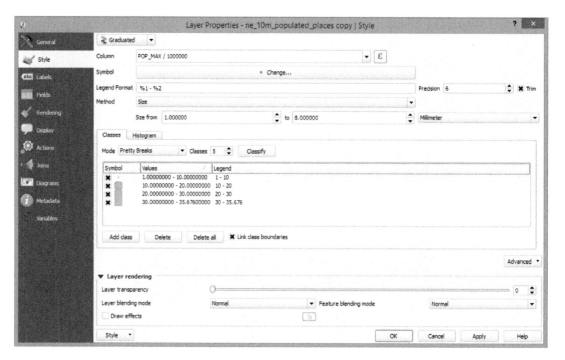

Figure 1.5: Layer properties

Figure 1.6: The map in the World Robinson projection

1.3   Finishing Touches

Increasing the maximum size of the symbols may make the map more compelling. Adjust the numbers in the Layer Properties such that the Size to is set to 12. This exaggerates the size of the circles more, which makes them more prominent and easier to see. Even larger sizes are possible, of course, however, the cartographer must balance the visual impact with the distinct possibility that the map readers may equate the symbol size with actual size. The finished map for this recipe, therefore, uses the more conservative approach of scaling the symbols from 1 to 12 only. The final map is shown, along with an inverted color scheme, at the beginning of this recipe.

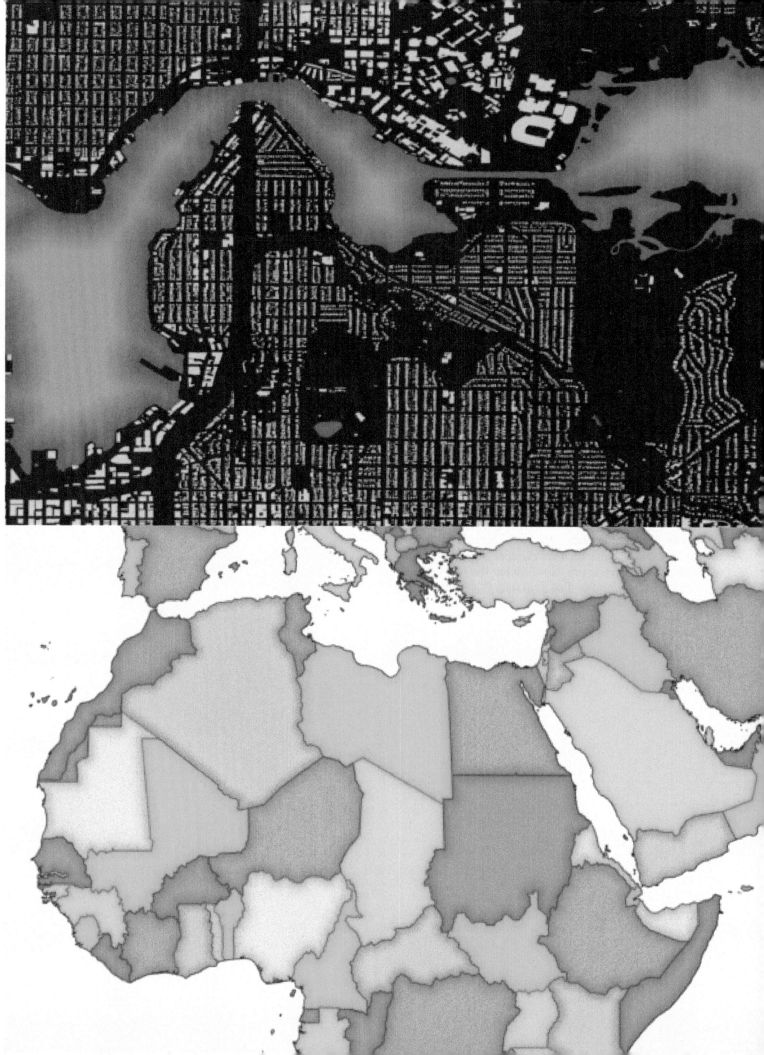

2. Shapeburst Fills for Water Features and More

In this section, we first make an avant-garde map of the Seattle area using the shapeburst fill functionality to create a spectacular vignette effect on the water features. Second, we use the same shapeburst technique in a more complicated retro-style design to evoke the look of an old school globe.

2.1 Introduction to the Shapeburst Fill

The part of the map you want your reader to look at (the figure) should be visually differentiated from background of the map (the ground). Honoring this Gestalt concept of figure-ground is easy in QGIS with the use of shapeburst fill symbology. In the first recipe we show how to use a shapeburst fill for water features so that shorelines appear to recede, thus enhancing the visual emphasis on the land features. In the second recipe we show how to use a shapeburst fill to provide differentiation between adjacent countries.

2.2 Seattle Building Map with Shoreline Shading

> To reproduce this map in QGIS, see the associated shapeburst_fills_A.qgs project.

Begin design of the map by adding the SpatialLite multipolygon layer from seattle_osm.db to the project. Examining the polygons, we can see there are more features displayed than we'd like to map. For this map we only want to display the water polygons and the building polygons.

In the Layer properties, General, Provider feature filter, Query Builder for the multipolygons layer, use the following query:

```
"building" IS NOT NULL
```

as shown in Figure 2.1.

Figure 2.1: Querying SpatialLite data

Notice how the field names and field values can be explored in the Query builder, which can be an important time-saver for determining how to select for only those features you're interested in, especially in large and complex datasets such as OpenStreetMap.

Rename the layer to buildings and then duplicate it. Rename the duplicated layer to water. Change the fill color for the buildings to hex #cccccc and the border style to No Pen. Similarly to the building layer, apply the following query to the water layer:

```
"natural" = 'water' OR "other_tags" =
'"waterway"=>"riverbank"'
```

Center the map on an interesting portion of the Seattle area. In our example map output we've zoomed in to the Lake Union area. To zoom into the same area, use View, Show Bookmarks, Import, locate QMD_Bookmarks in the resources folder and zoom to the Lake Union

Note that other ways of providing figure-ground differentiation exist such as using a contrasting shoreline color or incorporating a wavy-line symbology along the figure-ground border.

bookmark as shown in Figure 2.2 by double-clicking it in the bookmarks list.

Figure 2.2: The bookmarks window

In the water layer's Layer Properties, Style window, change the Symbol layer type to Shapeburst fill. In Gradient colors, Two-color change the first color to #225c5f and the second color to #389298. Also change the Shading style to Shade to a set distance of 10 millimeters as shown in Figure 2.3, on the facing page.

To finish up, change the background color of the map to #29002a and change the CRS to EPSG:102348. Both settings are found in the Project Properties dialog.

2.3   School Globe Style with Country Shading

> To reproduce this map in QGIS, see the associated shapeburst_fills_B.qgs project.

To setup this project, add ne_10m_ocean and ne_10m_admin_0_countries to a new, empty project. Set the ocean layer fill color to #f9fccc and set the Border style to No Pen.

The countries layer contains map color fields that assign each country a separate number such that no two numbers are adjacent. These numbers can then be mapped to distinct colors, giving each country a color fill that is not the same as any adjacent countries. In the Layer Properties, Style window, change the top drop-down to Categorized and use the Column MAPCOLOR7 (meaning that we'll render a maximum of 7 unique colors).

At this point the Color ramp can be assigned to Random colors or, if you'd prefer to use our color scheme, you can use the Style button to

load the shapeburst_countries_lower.qml style file as shown in Figure 2.4, on the next page.

Now make a duplicate of the countries layer. Click the Layer Properties, Style, Symbol, Change... button, click Simple fill (under Fill) in the left-hand side of this dialog, and change the Symbol layer type to Shapeburst fill. The first of the two gradient colors needs to be changed. Click the Expression button next to it, click Edit and type the expression @symbol_color into the Expression string builder. Click OK. Set the second color to transparent, the Shade to a set distance to 4 millimeters and the Blur strength to 10 as shown in Figure 2.5, on page 28.

This will create a shapeburst fill for each of the existing colors in the categories. Set the transparency for the entire layer to 30%.

The shading is a bit light near the edges of each polygon as shown in Figure 2.6, on page 28.

That's okay, but it might be better if we lessened that effect. Going back into the shapeburst fill expression for the first color, we can use an advanced method called **darker** by inserting the following expression:

```
darker(@symbol_color,150)
```

This changes the value portion of the color to 150, which effectively darkens all the colors in the categories simultaneously. However, we still have the problem where the shapeburst is fading toward black, whereas we'd like to vary only the alpha channel of the color. To fix this, use the following expression for the second color (instead of the transparent fill we set it to earlier):

```
set_color_part(@symbol_color,'alpha',0)
```

The result is shown in Figure 2.7, on page 28.

That completes the two recipes—the final result can be seen in the full page image at the beginning of this section.

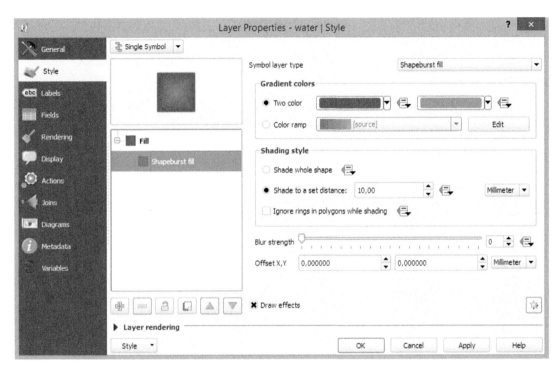

Figure 2.3: Creating a shapeburst fill for the water features

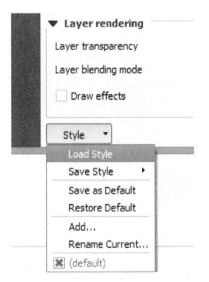

Figure 2.4: Load the custom seven color style here

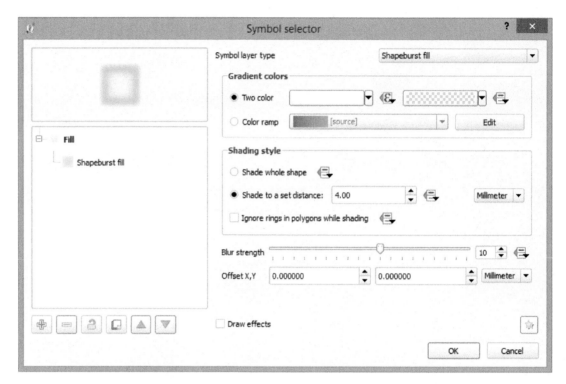

Figure 2.5: Changing all the colors in a categorized layer to shapeburst fills

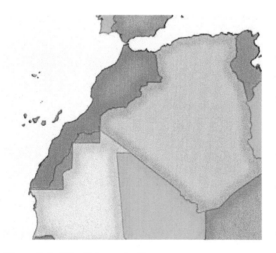

Figure 2.6: The lighter shading near country boundaries may be unintended

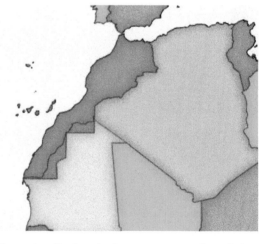

Figure 2.7: Darker shading near country boundaries

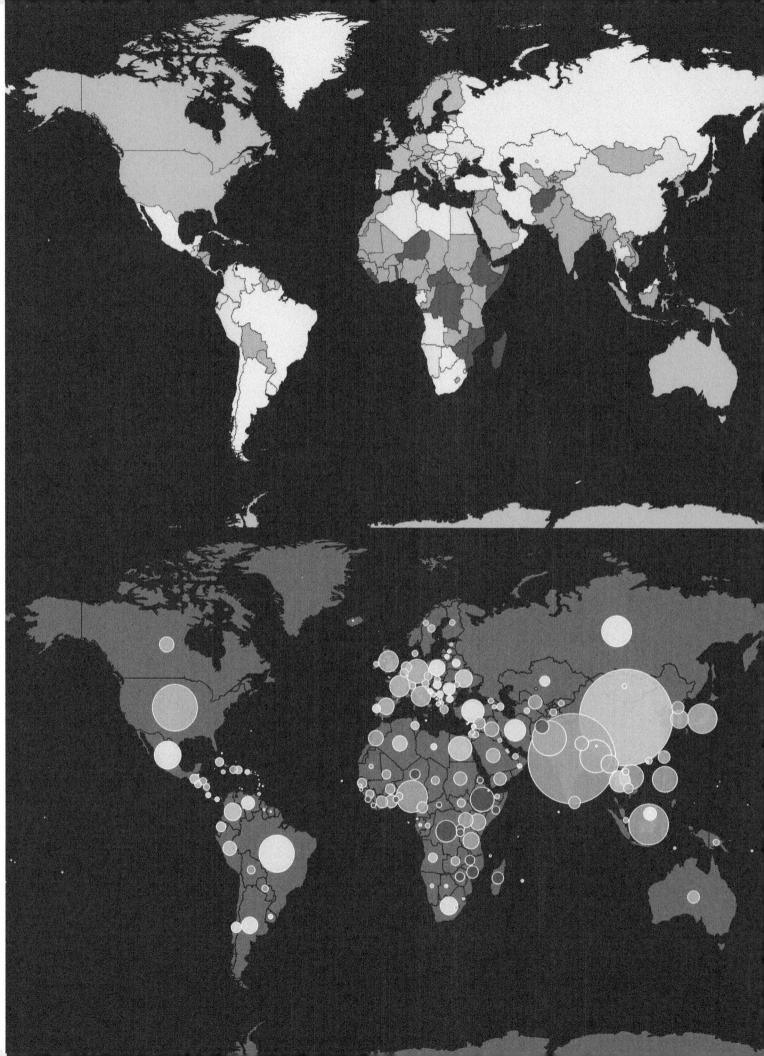

3. Mapping Economies Using GDP Choropleths or Scaled Symbols

In this recipe, we create a classed choropleth map illustrating the per capita gross domestic product (GDP) of the countries of the world.

> To reproduce this map in QGIS, open the choropleth_gdp.qgs project.

3.1 Introduction to Classed Choropleth Maps

Choropleths are a type of thematic map in which areas are shaded or patterned in proportion to a numerical attribute representing a rate or ratio, such as population density or per capita income. Never use choropleths for raw data or counts, such as country population or total GDP. Converting raw data and counts to rates, such as population per area unit or GDP per capita, is necessary, otherwise, all your map would show is that, on average, bigger countries have more inhabitants and a higher GPD than smaller countries.

A general rule of thumb is to stick to three to seven classes for classed choropleth maps. In this recipe, we use five classes to categorize the countries.

3.2 Exploring the Dataset

For this map, we load the:

ne_10m_admin_0_countries.shp

shapefile into QGIS.

This dataset contains data about country GDP (attribute GDP_MD_EST in million US Dollars) and population (attribute POP_EST). As shown in Figure 3.1, GDP_MD_EST ranges from -99 (unknown value) to 15094000 for the USA and similarly POP_EST ranges from -99 (unknown value) to 1338612968 for China. For our choropleth map, we use these two attributes to compute the GDP per capita:

GDP_MD_EST / POP_EST * 1000000

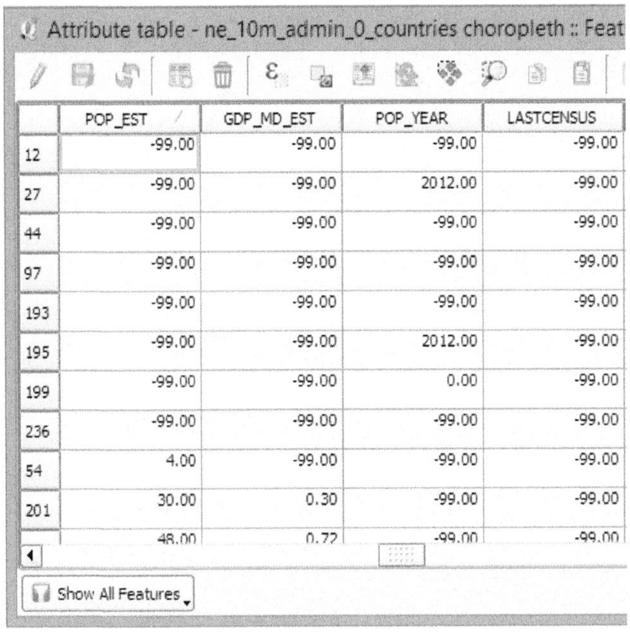

	POP_EST	GDP_MD_EST	POP_YEAR	LASTCENSUS
12	-99.00	-99.00	-99.00	-99.00
27	-99.00	-99.00	2012.00	-99.00
44	-99.00	-99.00	-99.00	-99.00
97	-99.00	-99.00	-99.00	-99.00
193	-99.00	-99.00	-99.00	-99.00
195	-99.00	-99.00	2012.00	-99.00
199	-99.00	-99.00	0.00	-99.00
236	-99.00	-99.00	-99.00	-99.00
54	4.00	-99.00	-99.00	-99.00
201	30.00	0.30	-99.00	-99.00
	48.00	0.72	-99.00	-99.00

Figure 3.1: GDP and population values

To create our choropleth map, we need to deal with the -99 (unknown) values. Additionally, we need to deal with outliers in our data with extraordinarily high GDP per capita, such as, the Vatican and Antarctica. A great way to visualize the distribution of values is the Histogram feature built into the Graduated renderer interface shown in Figure 3.2, on the following page.

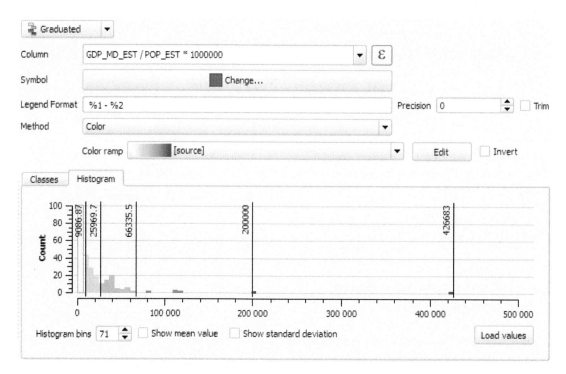

Figure 3.2: The histogram in the Graduated renderer interface visualizes the value distribution

3.3 Setting Up a Classed Choropleth Map

The outliers in our data throw off the automatic classification algorithms, such as **Natural Breaks**, which is often recommended for choropleth maps. Instead of relying on the automatic classification, we therefore define the classes manually. This gives us much more control over how things are classified. Since we also need to deal with the `-99` (unkown) values, we create a **Rule-based** renderer instead of a simple **Graduated** renderer.

To draw the countries with unknown GDP per capita in gray, we create a no data rule. Press the green **Add rule** button below the rule list to create a new rule and enter the following expression in the rule filter:

```
NOT (GDP_MD_EST > 0 AND POP_EST > 0)
```

Once the no data rule is set up, all other countries will fit the data rule, which is defined using the expression:

> The colors used in this recipe are based on a color ramp from Petersons's book "GIS Cartography", from top down: #a63e75, #eaa28a, #f9cd90, #c4ef6d, and #56a617. The nodata color is #8d8d8d and the map background is #163041).

```
GDP_MD_EST > 0 AND POP_EST > 0
```

We then divide the countries into five classes: under 1000, 5000, 10000, 20000 and, over 20000 Dollars. To create these classes, we can use the **Refine current rule | Add ranges to rule** functionality in the rule's context menu shown in Figure 3.3.

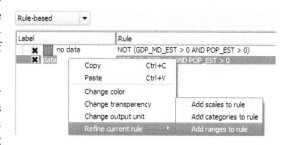

Figure 3.3: Refine the data rule

This opens a **Refine a rule to ranges** dialog (as shown in Figure 3.4, on the facing page) where we can create classes with the same user interface we already know from the **Graduated** renderer. Use the expression that calculates the GDP per capita and press **Classify**. Afterwards, just edit the class bounds and colors.

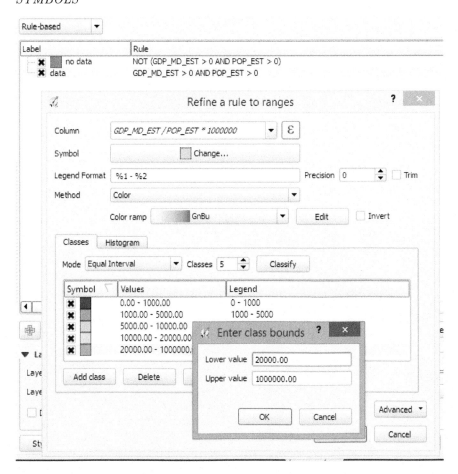

Figure 3.4: Customize the classes to your liking

With a little cleaning, the rule for "under 1000 Dollars" looks like this:

```
GDP_MD_EST / POP_EST * 1000000 > 0 AND
GDP_MD_EST / POP_EST * 1000000 <= 1000
```

The complete set of rules with manually edited labels is shown in Figure 3.5, on the next page.

Figure 3.6, on the following page shows the finished map in World Gall Stereographic (EPSG 54016) projection. One issue with this approach is that big countries and those further away from the equator appear more prominently on the map, irrespective of the number of people that are affected. In the second part of this recipe, we will address this issue using scaled circle symbols.

3.4 Scaled Circle Symbols

Using circle symbols, we visually relate the GDP per capita to the affected population instead of the affected area. This map design combines a clean global countries map in a uniform color with colorful circles, which are created using the Diagrams functionality in the Layer Properties. We use the same five-entry classification as in the classed choropleth map in order to keep the resulting maps comparable.

First, make sure the Diagram type is set to Pie chart. Then, we configure the diagram size. To scale the diagram size according to the affected population, we use the Scaled size option configured to the POP_EST attribute, as shown in Figure 3.7, on the next page.

Next, we want to make sure that all country diagrams are shown. To do this, activate the

It is useful to customize the rule labels in the renderer dialog because this way the rules will be labeled correctly in the layer list as well as in print map legends.

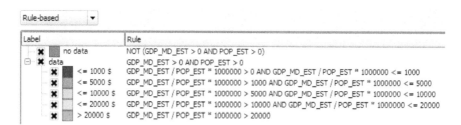

Figure 3.5: Complete set of rules for the choropleth map

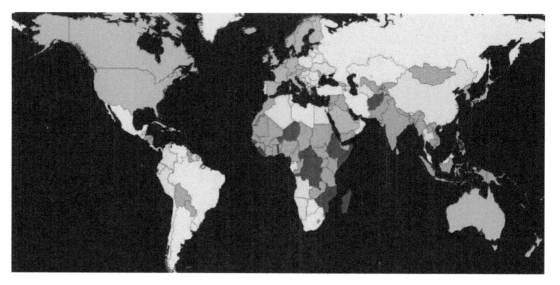

Figure 3.6: Final choropleth map

Figure 3.7: Diagram size scales with population

Show all diagrams option in the **Appearance** section. In addition, we set the **Placement** to **Over Centroid** (as shown in Figure 3.8) to ensure that diagrams are placed at a location that is easy to associate with the corresponding country.

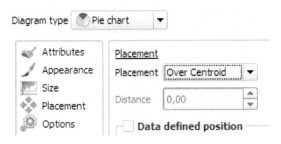

Figure 3.8: Place the diagrams on the country centroids

So far, these settings place an empty circle diagram (black outline only) into each country feature. In order to control the diagram fill color, we use the rule expressions we created for the choropleth map in the first part of this recipe. To add these expressions to the pie chart settings, as shown in Figure 3.9, on the next page, press the **Add expression** button. This opens the expression builder dialog where we can enter our expressions, such as:

```
GDP_MD_EST / POP_EST * 1000000 > 20000
```

for the highest GDP per capita class. To finish the configuration, we need to add the expressions, adjust the colors and customize the legend labels.

Once all five expressions are added, the diagrams will be filled with our class colors as shown in Figure 3.10, on the following page. The diagram placement algorithm makes sure that smaller diagrams are drawn on top of larger diagrams.

To finish the style, change the diagram **Line** color to white and set the **Transparency** to **20%** to make underlying country features shine through. The country features themselves are styled with a simple **Single Symbol** renderer in a neutral color.

This way of representing GDP per capita provides a much clearer perspective on the global economic situation and the affected population than the default choropleth map could provide.

This recipe uses diagrams rather than a centroid fill because currently the centroid fill renderer puts a centroid marker into each part of the multipart polygon.

The country color on this map is #486373.

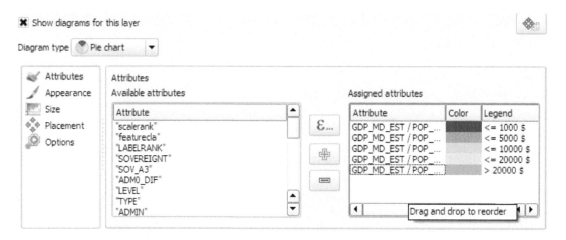

Figure 3.9: Diagram color depends on GDP per capita

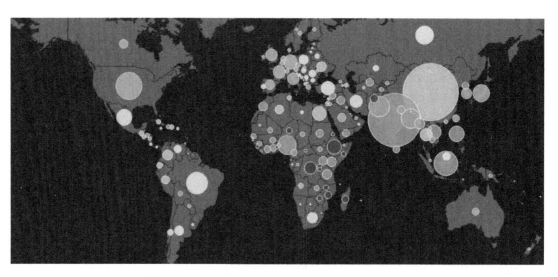

Figure 3.10: Final map with scaled circle symbols

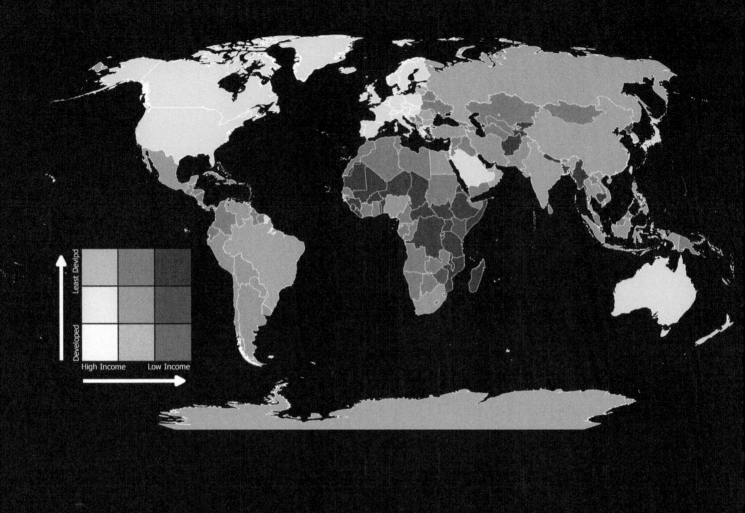

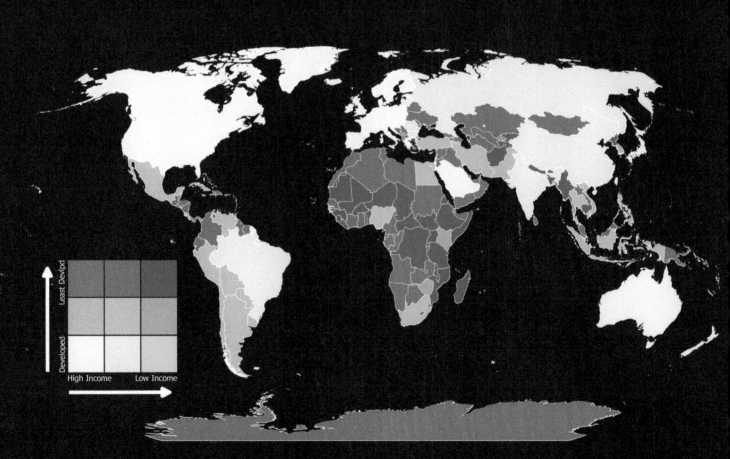

4. Mapping Economy and Income Using Bivariate Choropleths

The GDP Choropleth recipe illustrated how to use QGIS to apply a graduated color scheme to geographic features based on a variable. In this recipe, we'll show you how to create a more complex choropleth that shows two variables at the same time, with the color schemes blending together to create a bivariate visualization.

> To reproduce this map in QGIS, open the bivariate_choropleths.qgs project. To read more about bivariate choropleths, see Joshua Stevens' online tutorial entitled "Bivariate Choropleth Maps: a How-to Guide" at: http://loc8.cc/qmd/bichoropleth

4.1 Bivariate Choropleth Methods

There are two methods of creating bivariate choropleth maps in QGIS. One is with separate layers, each representing one of the variables classed and colored accordingly, with a multiply color blending mode applied to the top-most layer. The advantage of this method is it's comparatively easy. Another method is to combine both variables into a single layer in which all the possible combinations of colors are represented in a single field. The advantage with this method is that each of the blended colors can be easily tweaked. We'll show you both methods in this recipe.

Bivariate visualizations require a bit of up front thought. First, the two variables need to be placed into appropriate low, middle, and high categories for maps with 9 classes (or low and high categories for a total of four blended classes). We recommend no more than 9 to keep the map easy to read. The two graduated color schemes applied to these categories need to blend well while being quite visually distinct. For example, one variable might be depicted in a gray, light blue, dark blue scheme while the other could be depicted in a gray, light red, dark red

scheme. The low values or the high values (but not both) are the same hue for both variables and can be represented by white, gray, or some other neutral that works well with the map's background color. Two different color schemes are showcased here, one for Method 1 and the other for Method 2 as shown in Figure 4.1.

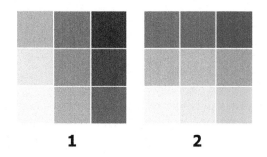

1   **2**

Figure 4.1: The two color palettes

4.2 Classifying the Data

We'll use the Natural Earth countries dataset for these methods. The two variables being mapped are in the fields ECONOMY and INCOME_GRP. These two fields contain strings but they begin with a number that encodes the low to high representation of the fields. In both methods we'll isolate these numbers in order to apply graduated color schemes to them. The following classification is used here:

```
Economy
1-2 Developed
3-5 Emerging
6-7 Least Developed
Income Group
1-2 High Income
3-4 Middle Income
5 Low Income
```

Note that the categorization here is subjective, with other categorizations possible (e.g., values

1 through 3 could be classified as Developed instead of just values 1 and 2).

To get started, add the following shapefile to a new project:

```
ne_10m_admin_0_countries.shp
```

Since it already has the fields and calculations in it that will be created in both Method 1 and Method 2, it is highly recommended that you make a copy of this shapefile and remove the following fields so that you can create them yourself as you follow along:

```
econnum
incomenum
econ1
income1
econincome
```

4.3   Method 1: Multiply

This method requires adding the cleaned country layer (see previous section) twice to a new QGIS project. Rename one of the country layers Economy and the other Income. The changes to the attribute table that we'll make will be reflected in both copies because they come from the same source data.

Open one of the attribute tables and add two new columns with the default specifications, one called econnum and the other incomenum.

Open the field calculator and update the econnum field to isolate just the numerical portion of the ECONOMY field, using the following expression:

```
to_int( left ( "ECONOMY", 1 ) )
```

Similarly, update the incomenum field using the following expression:

```
to_int( left ( "INCOME_GRP", 1 ) )
```

Now the layers can be styled. The Economy layer should be styled with a graduated color scheme on the econnum column with 3 classes. Change the colors, values, and legend entries for each symbol so that it appears as shown in Figure 4.2.

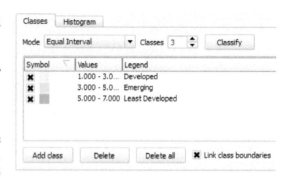

Figure 4.2: Classified economy information

The colors used for the symbols are #e8e8e8, #b0d5df, and #64acbe. In order to make sure that the country borders are visible but nonobtrusive, also change all three border colors for each category to white, 0.1 millimeters.

The Income layer should be styled with a graduated color scheme on the incomenum column with 3 classes. Change the colors, values, and legend entries for each symbol so that it appears as shown in Figure 4.3.

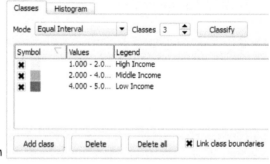

Figure 4.3: Classified income information

The colors used for the symbols are #e8e8e8, #e4acac, and #c85a5a. Change all three border colors for each category to white, 0.1 millimeters.

Return to the layer properties dialog for the economy layer, which should be above the income layer in the Layers Panel, and change the Style, Layer rendering, Layer blending mode to Multiply. This effectively combines the colors from the economy layer with the colors from the income layer to produce a blended color scheme with up to 9 possible final colors.

This visualization, as shown in Figures 4.4 and 4.5 (one with a white background and one with a black background), highlights countries with both a developed economy and high income (gray) and countries with the least development and low income (dark brown). However, it also shows some other interesting cases such as where there are relatively high incomes but less development (solid blue), perhaps indicating countries where development has not yet caught up with income.

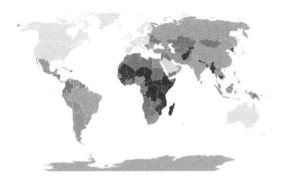

Figure 4.4: Method 1 results on a white background

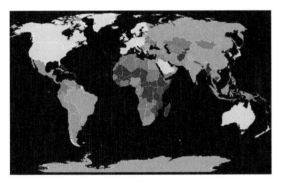

Figure 4.5: Method 1 results on a black background

4.4 Method 2: Data Driven

If you've just completed Method 1, you may want to separate it so that it is in its own layer group and then make a copy of one of the layers outside of that layer group. This new layer could be renamed to `Method2;Economy`. Open the layer and add two new fields called `econ1` and `income1`. In Method 1 we let the classifier do the work of translating the numbers into the low, medium, high categories, but in this method we need to manually classify them by giving them a number of 3, 2, or 1, respectively.

Use the following expression in the field calculator to update the `econ1` field:

```
CASE WHEN "econnum" > 5 THEN 3
  WHEN "econnum" <= 5 AND "econnum" > 3 THEN 2
  ELSE 1
END
```

Similarly, use the following expression in the field calculator to update the `income1` field:

```
CASE WHEN "incomenum" > 4 THEN 3
  WHEN "incomenum" <= 4
    AND "incomenum" > 2 THEN 2
  ELSE 1
END
```

Save the edits to the attribute table and then create a new text (string) field in the field calculator called `econincome` to concatenate the two new fields into a single number that will now represent both the categorized economy status and the categorized income status:

```
concat("econ1",tostring("income1"))
```

Save the field changes, stop editing, and go the **Layer properties** to change the style to categorized, on column `econincome`, and click **Classify**. The style should appear as shown in Figure 4.6.

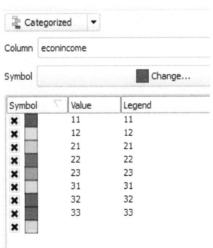

Figure 4.6: Classified economy and income information combined, before customization

Notice that the resulting categorization is missing the category 13 (i.e., developed, low income), which is because there aren't any features in this category. To maintain consistency in the legend, add this category manually by editing the catch-all category that doesn't have Value or Legend text by double-clicking its Value and Legend sections and typing 13 for both. Next, click the Value heading to sort the values. Now you can apply the color scheme found in `bivariate_choropleths_method2.qml` using the Style, Load menu found at the bottom of the Layer properties window. The completed style should appear as shown in Figure 4.7.

These steps are also illustrated in the print composer titled "bonus" in the QGIS project file.

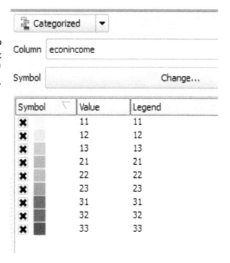

Figure 4.7: Classified economy and income information combined, with loaded color scheme

4.5 Bonus Material: Bivariate Legends

While it isn't currently possible to create a blended legend with the legend tool for maps such as the one created in Method 1, a suggested work-around is to use the Print composer, Add shape, Add rectangle tool in a gridded print composer layout and, using the Pick color tool as shown in Figure 4.8, on the facing page, manually apply the colors from the legend. (Note the color picker is not available on OSX.)

Essentially, once the main colors are copied over into the matrix, copy and paste them into the four empty spaces with the blues layered on top of the reds. This is much easier if the View, Show Grid and View, Snap to grid options are turned on. At this point the reds will not be visible underneath the blues. For the four rectangles that need to be blended, use the Item properties, Rendering, Blending mode, Multiply tool as shown in Figure 4.9, on the next page.

Specifically, create nine squares in a grid where the first vertical column shows the colors from the top-most layer in the map and the lowest horizontal column shows the colors from the bottom layer in the map (A). The lower-left square shares the same color with both map layers. Next, copy the color from the lower middle square into the rest of the squares in that vertical column and do the same for the lower-right color (A).

Next, copy the rectangle and color from the left-middle square and paste it onto the other squares in that horizontal column, on top of the existing rectangles. Do the same for the top-left square (B). Then apply color blending, multiply, to the four rectangles that are on top in the upper-right quadrant (C). Add arrows and text for explanatory material and the legend is complete. See Figure 4.10, on the facing page.

The finished maps for both method 1 and method 2, along with their legends, are shown at the beginning of this recipe.

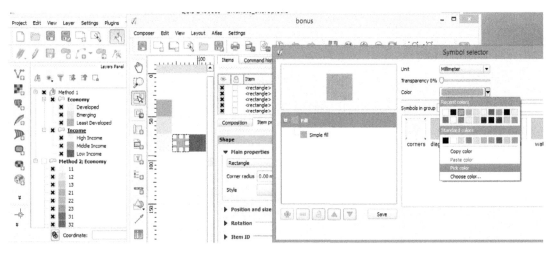

Figure 4.8: Setting up the windows so that the colors can be copied easily from the map to the print composer rectangles

Figure 4.9: Using the multiply blending mode on the top-most rectangle

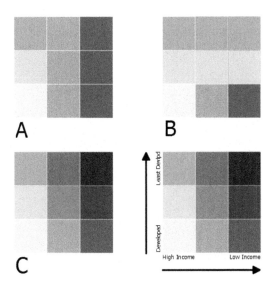

Figure 4.10: Process for creating a bivariate choropleth legend in the print composer

In this recipe we'll create a map of downtown Seattle coffee shop locations that has a subtly hand-drawn appearance. While the background map information will look like a typical map, the coffee shop icons themselves have some calligraphic flare. This recipe will be the basis for the Text Buffers recipe which then becomes the basis for the Basic Layout recipe.

> To reproduce this map in QGIS, open the `custom_svgs.qgs` project.

5.1 Prepare the Background

Adding a couple of OpenStreetMap layers to the project—filtered for the specific data required—will give us the background information for our map. First, add the water data from the `seattle_osm.db` database multipolygons table as a SpatialLite layer. Use the **Query Builder** dialog that opens when you double-click the multipolygons item listing (also found via the **Set Filter** button) to filter the multipolygons before adding them to the project with the following expression:

```
"natural" = 'water'
```

Click OK and add it to the map. Change the fill color for the water layer to a gray with a hint of blue `#d4d8dd` and the border to `#728584`. Also change the background color (land) to a coffee color like `#cd9a63` in the **Project Properties**.

With the basic background in place, change the map's CRS to `EPSG:102348` and then zoom to the area around the Seattle ferry terminals in downtown Seattle at roughly `386854,68228`.*

Now add another SpatialLite layer, this time from the OpenStreetMap lines table using the following expression:

```
"highway" NOT NULL
```

We'd like the roads to appear subtly above the land. One technique for this is to give the feature a color that is somewhat lighter than the underlying feature. To do this, change the road layer color with the eye dropper tool in the **Pick color** drop-down option in **Layer Properties**. Mouse over the land color with the eye dropper and click. In OSX, copy and paste the hex value instead. Then go back to the color selector and lighten the color by changing the value from 80% to 90% as shown in Figure 5.1.

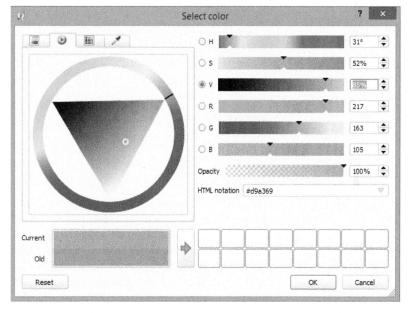

Figure 5.1: Changing the Value property to create a lighter color of the same hue

Increase the line width to 0.7 as well to add some heft to the roads. Now we're ready to put the coffee shop locations on the map.

* Try changing the scale to 1:5,000 and then typing this into the coordinate box to the left of the scale box.

5.2   Adding Coffee Shop Icons

Inkscape is a good software product for designing your own SVG format icons, but you can also find free icons or buy icons.

Since we're interested in branding this map with special coffee shop icons, we'll use an SVG (a common icon file type) that was created especially for this exercise. QGIS allows you to load any SVG to display for point data and change its size, but typically you can't change its color. One work-around would be to ensure that your SVG is the right color for the map when you create it or download it. However, what if you'd like to change the color later once you've started creating a map? What if you'd like the same SVG to be in different colors based on attribute type?

To solve these problems, you can edit the SVG file in a text editor to allow QGIS to change its colors. Showcasing this technique is the purpose of this exercise. (You might notice that you can already change the color of the icons in this recipe's project file. This is because the project file showcases the finished recipe with the icons that are already parameterized as per the steps below).

First, add the coffee data by adding another SpatialLite layer from the seattle_osm.db points table with the following filter:

```
"other_tags" LIKE "%coffee%"
```

Using the Test option in the Query builder should return 190 rows—go ahead and add it to the map. To style the coffee shop layer, we need to add the coffee shop SVG icon. In the Layer Properties, Style, Symbol layer type drop-down, change the marker from Simple marker to SVG marker as shown in Figure 5.2, on the facing page.

This is where we see many available icons that come with QGIS. Underneath the existing icons, there is a place to load your own. Click the ellipsis under the SVG Image box as shown in Figure 5.3, on the next page.

Navigate to the resources/coffee.svg file and click Open. (Note, for this step, don't use resources/coffeeParam.svg. That file is used in the completed project file for this recipe to show how the map looks once this recipe is complete). Change the size to 10 and apply

the changes. The QGIS project should now look similar to that shown in Figure 5.4, on the facing page.

It would be nice to use a different color for these coffee mugs than the default blue. In fact, we'd like to use green for Starbucks locations and black for all other coffee shops. However, if you return to the layer properties you'll notice—unlike with other marker symbols—the color options will not change This is because the color is hard-coded into the SVG file by default. We'd like to change that by adding a parameter to the coffee.svg file.

To parameterize the SVG, first make a copy of the svg file (we've called our copy coffeeParam.svg and you can find it in the resources folder for reference). Open the newly copied SVG file in a text editor. Replace the portion of the path style information that is found at the beginning of the path tag as shown here:

```
<path
    style="fill:#006978;fill-opacity:1"
```

with our own parameterized code as shown here:

```
<path
        fill="param(fill)
    #FFF" stroke="param(outline) #000"
    stroke-width="param(outline-width) 1"
```

You can also find the code above to copy and paste in resources/svgParam.txt. Save the changes to the file and close it. Now go back to the QGIS project and this time load the new SVG file that you just modified (or load coffeeParam.svg, which already has the modified code). Notice that you can now change the color of the coffee mug in the border color picker.

Figure 5.2: Changing from a Simple marker to an SVG marker style

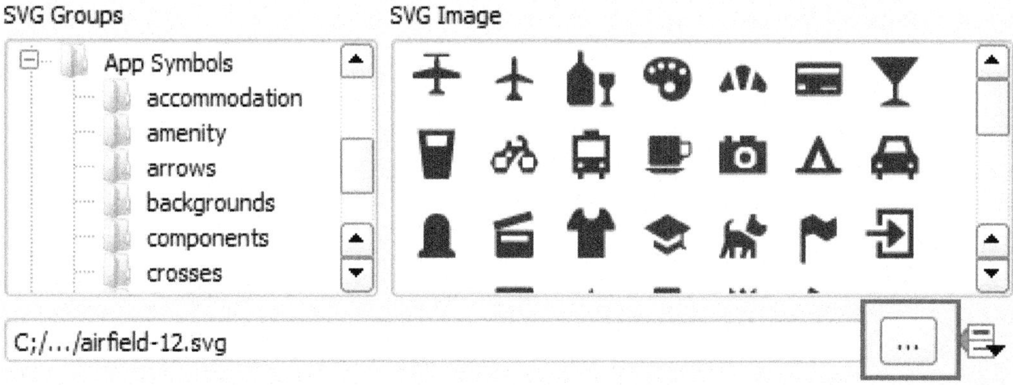

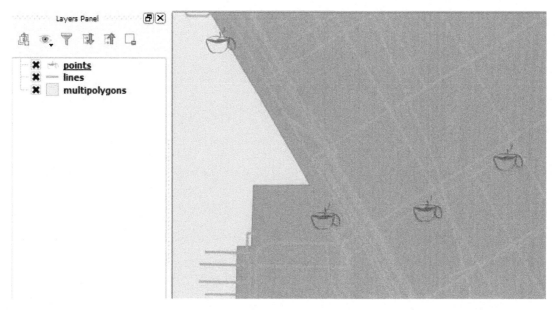

Figure 5.3: Load your own SVG file here

Figure 5.4: The coffee mug icon added to the project in its default color

5.3 Bonus: Rule-based Styling

This section illustrates how to create separate symbology for features in the same dataset. GIS users might be familiar with achieving this result by simply making a second copy of the dataset in order to style it differently. That method decreases the project's performance, however, which is why single-layer, rule-based styling is preferred in QGIS.

To show how this is done, we'll create green coffee mugs for the Starbucks coffee shops and black coffee mugs for the other coffee shops. In Layer properties, Style choose the Rule-based choice from the upper most drop-down menu as shown in Figure 5.5.

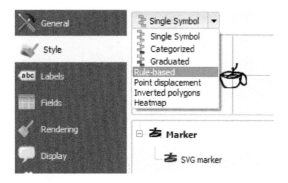

Figure 5.5: Changing to rule-based styling

This brings up a dialog in which to list the rule-based styles, though at this point there is only one. Copy and paste the first item so that there are two identical rules. Right-click the item to copy and paste and see the other available options. Double-click the first item to bring up the Rule properties and label it Starbucks. Click the ellipsis next to the filter box to create a filter expression based on the data. We'll use this for the first rule:

```
"name" = 'Starbucks'
```

See Figure 5.6, on the facing page.

Once the filter has been set, change the color for this symbol to #00592D. Remember to change both the fill and outline colors and then click OK. That completes the first rule. The second rule should be labeled Other with the following filter:

```
"name" <> 'Starbucks`
```

This one can be left black. See the finished map at the beginning of this recipe for the final results.

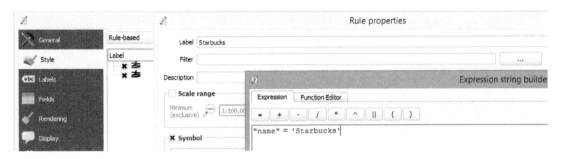

Figure 5.6: Filtering data with "rules" in order to symbolize different data with different symbology

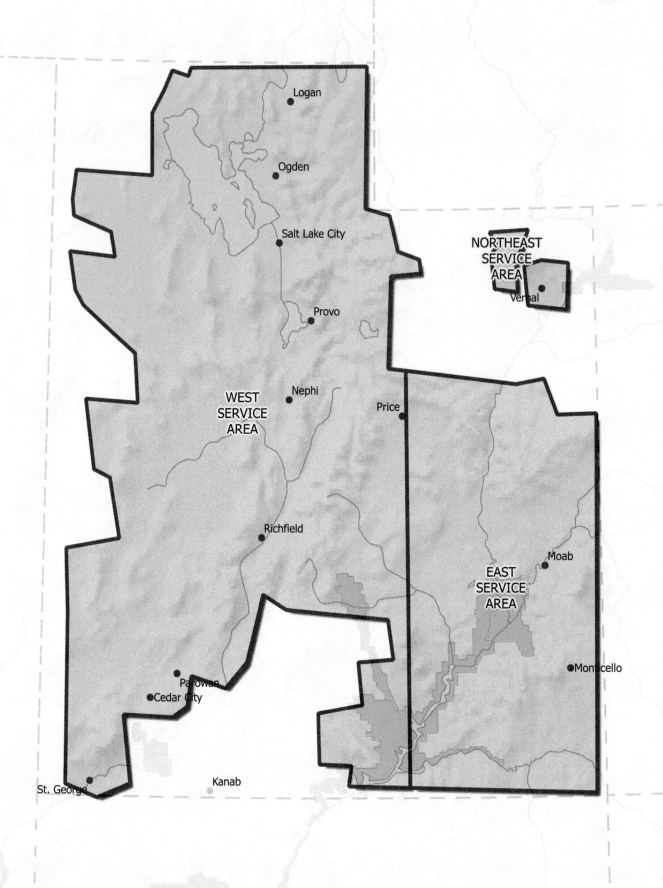

Logan

Ogden

Salt Lake City

Provo

WEST
SERVICE
AREA

Nephi

Price

Richfield

Parowan

Cedar City

Kanab

St. George

NORTHEAST
SERVICE
AREA

Vernal

Moab

EAST
SERVICE
AREA

Monticello

6. Highlighting Areas with Inverted Polygons

In this recipe we'll make use of the inverted polygons renderer to create a map that highlights a fictional service area while also depicting the surrounding geography in a more subtly rendered fashion to provide geographic context.

> To reproduce this map in QGIS, open the highlight_area.qgs project.

6.1 Setting Up the Map

This map contains quite a few data layers. We'll add GRAY_LR_SR_OB first to put it at the bottom of the layer list where it needs to be for this map. Continue to add the other data layers in the order listed:

```
GRAY_LR_SR_OB
ne_10m_parks_and_protected_lands_area
ne_10m_rivers_north_america
ne_10m_rivers_lake_centerlines
ne_10m_lakes
ne_10m_lakes_north_america
ne_10m_populated_places
ne_10m_admin_1_states_provinces
```

Change the projection to EPSG:3677 (Utah Central) and zoom to the Utah area (e.g., by selecting and zooming to name=Grand Canyon in the parks layer and adjusting from there, or by eye).

We don't stick with the default styling of the hillshade layer in this map. Instead, you need to customize it so it becomes a subtle elevation indicator that doesn't overwhelm the map. To accomplish this, first lighten the layer to an overall transparency of 50%. Also colorize it with a strength of 60% and change the hue to a peachy-brown (#e9aa5c) as shown in Figure 6.1, on the next page.

The protected lands are styled green with no border. The lakes and rivers are all the same blue color with a slighter darker blue border.

The populated places are small, black, round dots with simple labels restricted to just Utah by filtering it with the following expression:

```
"ADM1NAME" = 'Utah'
```

Future QGIS releases may provide the ability to mask labels as well, but for now labels draw on top of the layer styling, meaning that if the populated places labels weren't restricted to Utah, all labels would appear to have the same hierarchy including those residing outside the focus area.

The states layer is symbolized with a fairly wide, custom, dark gray dashed line. The wider dashed line is styled by changing the Layer properties, Style, Symbol layer type drop-down menu to Outline, Simple Line and changing the Use custom dash pattern as shown in Figure 6.2, on page 53.

The layers panel will now look as shown in Figure 6.3, on page 53. If the layers aren't already in the same order, rearrange them now.

At this point we've got a nice looking basemap of the general area as shown in Figure 6.4, on page 53.

6.2 Styling with Inverted Polygons

Now, add the highlight_service_area.shp shapefile to take a look at the area that will be the main focus of the map. This shapefile depicts a fictional service area, perhaps for a power company. Our goal is to focus the map reader's attention on the service area and de-emphasize locations outside of it while still providing sufficient geographic context in the surrounding areas. A simple service area outline might suffice but it doesn't give the robust emphasis we're after. It's tempting to approach this by creating all new layers clipped to the service area but that is extremely time consuming.

Since there are a few datasets in this project that have the same styles, try using the Copy and Paste Style functionality by right-clicking a data layer and using the Styles sub-menu.

Labels are discussed in detail in the Labels section of the book and can be skipped at this time if desired.

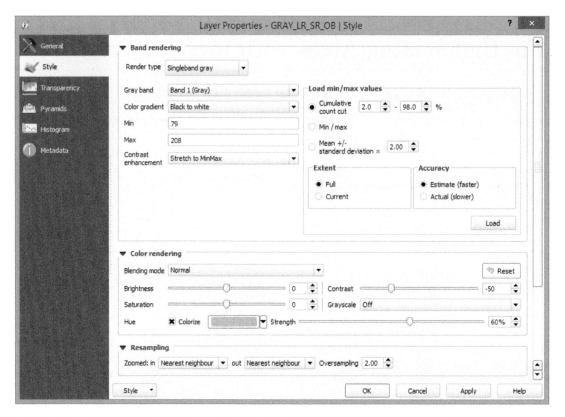

Figure 6.1: The raster style for the GRAY_LR_SR_OB layer, with changes made to the Hue and Strength

Instead, we'll employ the *Inverse polygon* technique. Applying inverse polygons to the service area layer gives us the ability to style the area *outside* the service area rather than the service area polygon itself. This is very useful for polygon layers that delineate a focus area but that don't have polygons around them, such as, for example, an archaeological site, a watershed, or a fire perimeter. (A polygon layer with polygons surrounding the focus area could simply be filtered for all polygons except the focus area in order to apply a transparency effect on the non-focus-area polygons.)

Style the service area layer with the Inverted polygons renderer, a white fill, a 1 millimeter black border, and, if you'd like to take this to an extra fancy level, an inner shadow draw effect. To make the inner shadow, check Draw Effects, click the yellow star to the right, then choose the Inner Shadow option. Also give it a layer transparency of 30% as shown in Figure 6.5, on page 54.

The finished map, as shown at the beginning

of this recipe, really does a good job of focusing our attention on the service areas. The finished map includes a few extra labels—the fictional service area names—just to make it a little more relatable as a finished map. However, since labels aren't introduced until the Labels section of the book, it's okay to leave those off.

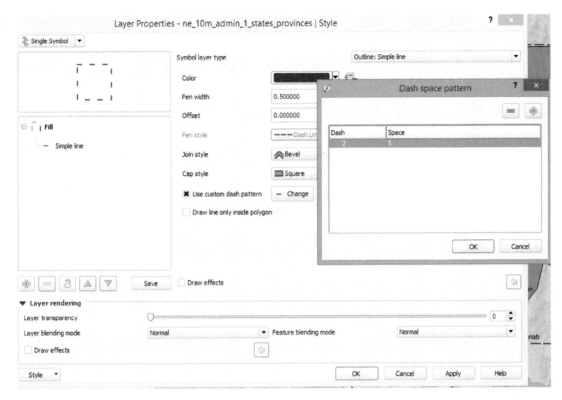

Figure 6.2: Dash space patterns can be adjusted after changing the Symbol layer type to Outline, Simple line and checking the box next to Use custom dash pattern

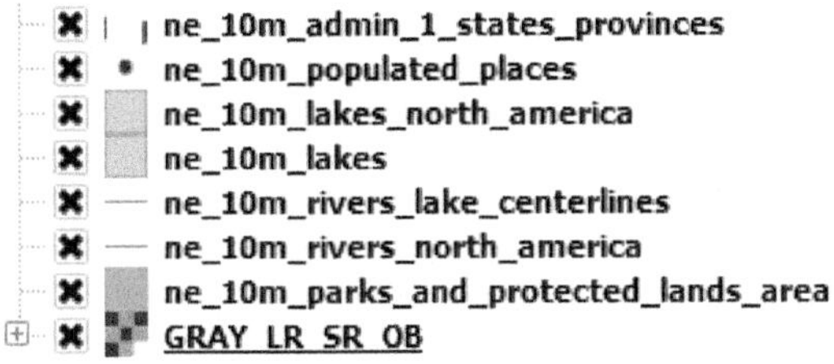

ne_10m_admin_1_states_provinces
ne_10m_populated_places
ne_10m_lakes_north_america
ne_10m_lakes
ne_10m_rivers_lake_centerlines
ne_10m_rivers_north_america
ne_10m_parks_and_protected_lands_area
GRAY_LR_SR_OB

Figure 6.3: The layers and styles

Figure 6.4: Earth toned basemap

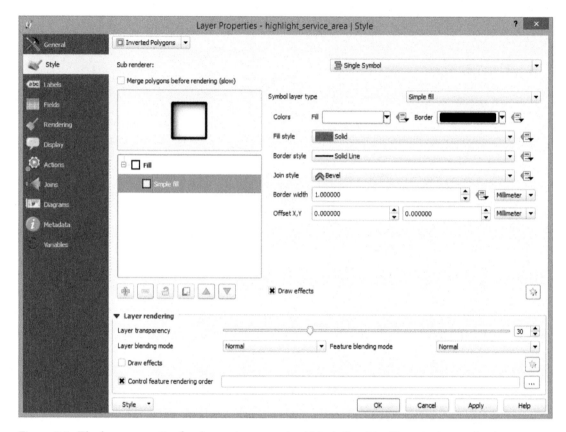

Figure 6.5: The layer properties for the service areas should look like this. Note the inverted polygons choice at upper-left and the activation of draw effects.

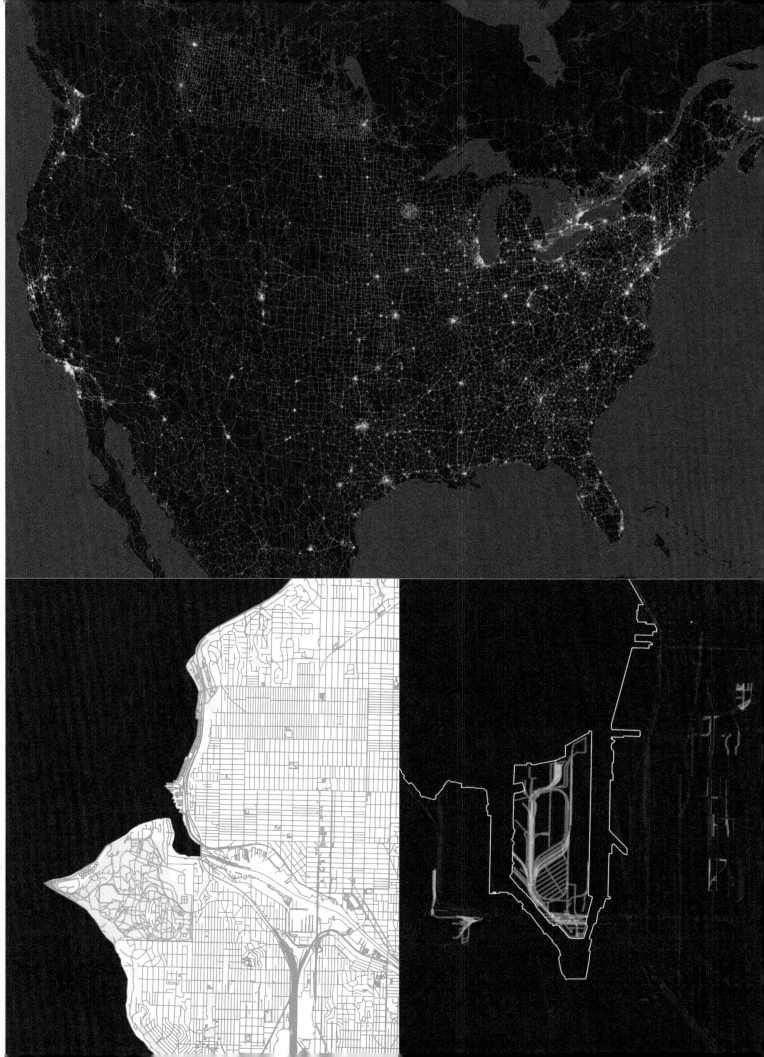

7. Color Blending

Color blending on the feature level is a great way to emphasize density (and deemphasize sparseness) in feature-rich datasets that contain a multitude of overlapping geometries. Similarly, color blending on the layer level is very useful as a way to emphasize areas of one dataset that overlap with another dataset.

This recipe showcases some map designs that are made possible by using the QGIS color blending modes on both the feature level and the layer level.

7.1 Blending Features with Addition

To reproduce this map in QGIS, open the color_blending_A.qgs project.

To highlight areas of high road density in North America, a brightness, or glow, effect is applied to a road dataset using the feature blending mode called Addition on a highly contrasting color palette. To set up this map, add the following layers to the QGIS project:

```
ne_10m_lakes
ne_10m_roads_north_america
ne_10m_admin_0_countries
```

Set the countries layer to black and the lakes and project background to dark gray. This will provide a nice base for optimal highlighting of the road density. Set the roads to blue with a line width of 0.15 and zoom to the U.S. in an appropriate projection. Here we've used EPSG 102003 Albers Equal Area Conic. Take a look at the map at this stage to see what it looks like without color blending. This is shown in Figure 7.1.

Now set the roads feature blending mode to Addition in the Layer properties, Style sub-menu as shown in Figure 7.2, on the next page. This map now highlights areas of increased road den-

Figure 7.1: The roads map without color blending

sity such as Los Angeles and New York City as shown in Figure 7.3, on the following page.

These parameters worked well for this dataset at this scale. However, there is a lot of leeway here with respect to line width, color, and transparency, so it's a good idea to try many combinations to get the look you desire. We didn't use transparency at all, for example, but combining it with color blending can become important when millions of features are in the dataset.

See the QGIS documentation for information on the color blending modes not mentioned in this recipe.

We also caution that density inferences must be made on complete datasets. In the example here, if the roads dataset were sparse in some locations due to the data being incomplete rather than due to actual road sparseness then this would possibly lead your map readers to some erroneous conclusions.

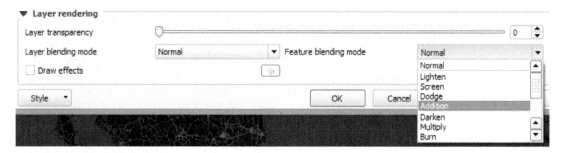

Figure 7.2: Selecting the addition feature blending mode

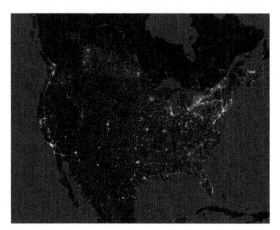

Figure 7.3: The finished roads map with addition feature blending mode applied

7.2 Blending Layers with Multiply

> To reproduce this map in QGIS, open the color_blending_B.qgs project.

Next we'll use the OpenStreetMap dataset to illustrate layer blending. Layer blending is much the same as feature blending, except it's generally applied to an entire layer in order to blend with underlying layers.

The background of this map is set to black and the OpenStreetMap database's multipolygon water designation is inverted and set to white to represent land. To do this, add the OpenStreetMap multipolygons via the SpatialLite importer, using the water tag in the Query Builder. (In OpenStreetMap parlance "natural=water" is actually called a "tag"). Use the Inverted Polygons symbolizer to color the non-water area white.

Add all of the lines from the OpenStreetMap database to the project to represent roads—this will be a line layer that should be styled blue with a width of 0.5. Set the map scale to approximately 1:20,000.

Now add the parks to the project. Parks are tagged leisure=park in the database. Style them yellow and make sure they're underneath the lines and the land is underneath both. Right now the map looks something like that shown in Figure 7.4.

Figure 7.4: The parks map without color blending

In the Layer properties, style, Layer rendering sub-menu for the lines (roads) layer, change the layer blending mode to multiply as shown in Figure 7.5, on the facing page.

Once this is applied, the blue lines that overlap the yellow parks now appear as green, while the blue lines that overlap with the white land continue to appear as blue. Essentially, the pixels from the line layer were multiplied with the pixels underneath them. The result is shown in Figure 7.6, on the next page.

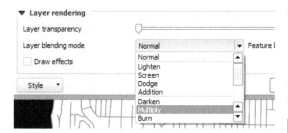

Figure 7.5: Selecting the multiply layer blending mode

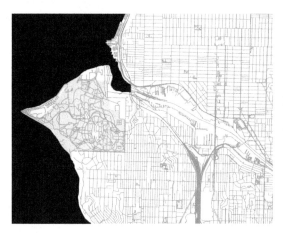

Figure 7.6: The finished parks map with multiply layer blending mode applied

7.3 Blending Layers with Dodge

To reproduce this map in QGIS, open the color_blending_B.qgs project.

The dodge blending mode is used in this example to highlight roads within industrial areas. Dodge essentially increases the brightness of the features underneath the dodge layer if the dodge layer itself is brighter than the underlying features. For this example, duplicate the line layer from the previous example, change its color to red, change its transparency to 90%, and leave everything else the same.

The lines are quite faint at this stage. Create a white coastline for context by duplicating the inverted water layer (i.e., land) from the previous map, changing it to simple fill instead of inverted polygons, and changing the border to white and the fill to transparent. Place the lines underneath the coastline.

To add in the industrial area polygons, use the OpenStreetMap database with landuse=industrial as the tag and position the industrial polygons between the coastline and lines. Use a yellow fill with no outline. The map will appear as shown in Figure 7.7.

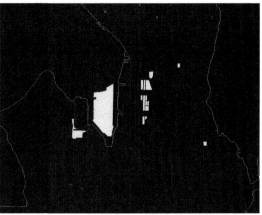

Figure 7.7: The industrial map without color blending

Now change the style of the industrial polygons so the layer blending mode is set to Dodge. The lines within the industrial areas have a prominent orange glow now, serving to highlight those roads without the industrial polygons dominating the map as shown in Figure 7.8.

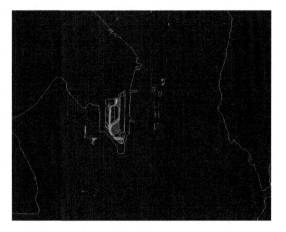

Figure 7.8: The finished industrial map with dodge layer blending mode applied

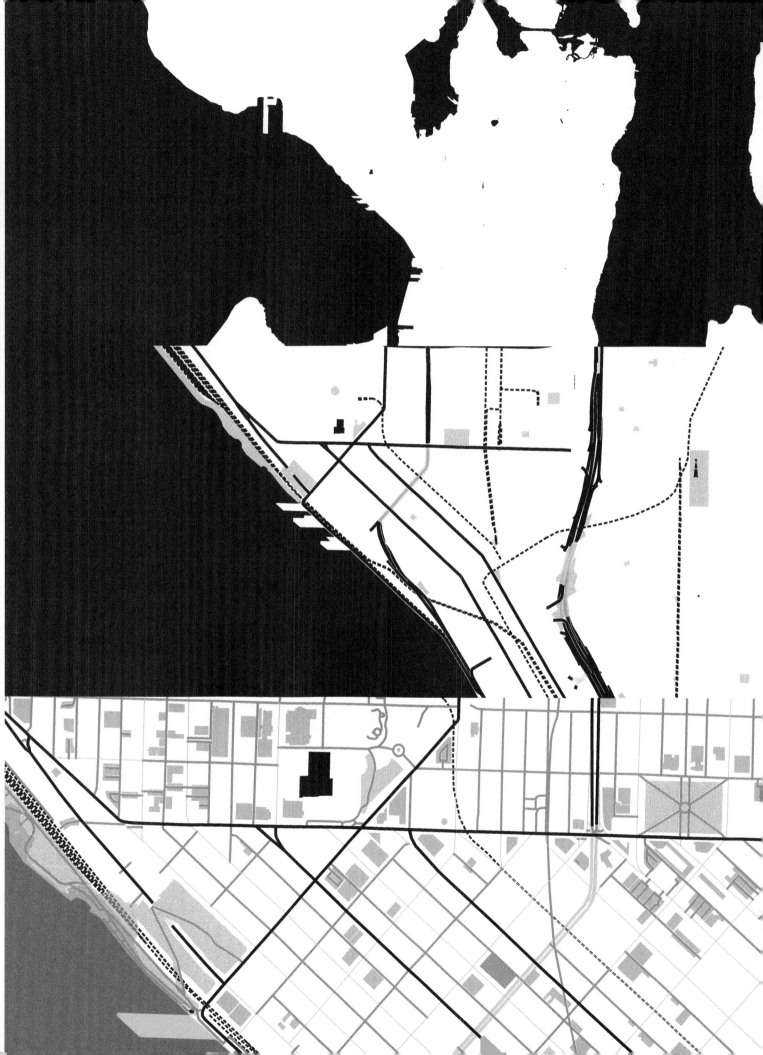

8. Working With Scale

Creating scale dependent rendering so that entire layers, or even certain features within layers, are only visible at particular scales is fairly easy with QGIS.

In this recipe we'll create a Seattle-area basemap with which to showcase building polygons and floodplain polygons at larger scales (high zooms), parks at medium scales (medium zooms), and just water and land at smaller scales (lower zooms). A roads layer is also included in which no roads are shown at smaller scales, main roads are shown at medium scales, and all roads are displayed at larger scales.

The terms "small scale" and "large scale" are relative. Since "small scale" is most commonly applied to scales of 1:250,000 and smaller, and since in this recipe we're working with scales of 1:100,000 and larger, we'll use the terms "smaller scale" and "larger scale" to differentiate the scales in this recipe.

> To reproduce this map in QGIS, open the working_with_scale.qgs project.

8.1 Basic Map for Smaller Scales

We want the water and land features to appear at all scales. We'll use the seattle_osm.db multipolygons table for the water features but instead of querying the data table for water immediately, add all the multipolygons as a single layer and use rule-based rendering to symbolize the water as shown in Figure 8.1. Make the water black and set the project background to white to serve as the land representation.

Figure 8.1: The water rule added to the multipolygons layer

Since the water and land need to appear at all scales, there is no need to do anything else with these.

8.2 More Detail for Larger Scales

In this section we're aiming for a project with layers and styling as seen in Figure 8.2, on the next page (shown at a medium scale relative to the other scales we're working with). Essentially, once the user of the QGIS project zooms in to 1:50,000 and larger, the main roads and parks need to appear as shown. Then, at a scale of 1:10,000 and larger, all the roads in the dataset, amenities, and floodplains need to appear.

First, add the fldplain_500yr.shp shapefile to the project. This contains the floodplain polygons. Since the floodplains should only be visible at scales of 1:10,000 and larger, set these parameters in the Layer properties, General, Scale dependent visibility section as shown in Figure 8.3, on the following page. This is where scale dependent visibility is set at the layer level.

Now set the park polygon visibility at the feature level instead of at the layer level. To do this, add the parks into the multipolygons layer that's already in the project and use the following filter in the rule-based dialog:

```
"leisure" = 'park'
```

and apply a fill style of Dense 6 with no border as shown in Figure 8.4, on page 63.

Opening the park rule properties (by double-clicking the item in the list) again reveals a scale range selector much the same as the one found in the General sub-menu, except this one will apply only to the parks and not to all the styles in the layer. Set the parks scale range from 1:50,000 (Minimum) to 1:1,000 (Maximum). Now zoom in and out in the project window to see how the floodplains and parks turn on and

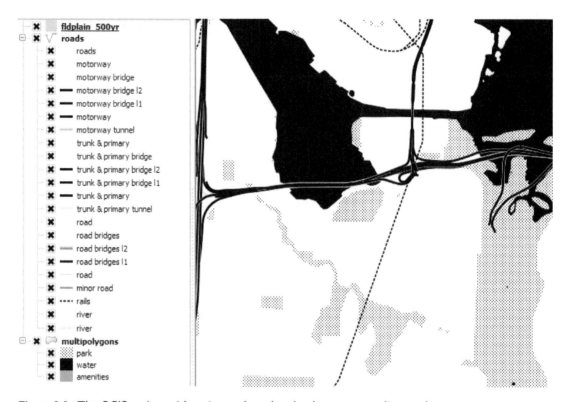

Figure 8.2: The QGIS project with major roads and parks shown at a medium scale

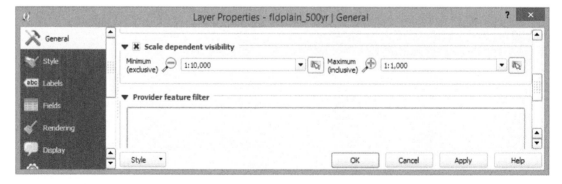

Figure 8.3: Scale constraints can be set in the general sub-menu in the layer properties

Figure 8.4: The parks rule added to the multipolygons layer

off depending on the scale, while the water and land are always visible.

Now we'll add the amenity building footprints into the project via the same multipolygons layer by adding another rule with the filter:

`"amenity" is not null`

This returns several thousand features and slows the rendering at smaller scales. To fix that, set the amenity scale range to 1:10,000 to 1:1,000 while also setting the style to red, no border, and 60% transparency as shown in Figure 8.5, on the following page.

An alternate way to set the scale is to type it in on the rule-based style dialog as shown in Figure 8.6, on the next page.

The roads layer is from the `seattle_osm.db` lines table and has some complex rule-based rendering. We won't go over each of these rules, instead, have a look at the `working_with_scale_roads.qml` file. Load this into the lines layer. The important thing to note here is that the minimum and maximum scale is set for all the rules in the qml file and that, with rule hierarchies such as these, the scale can be set at either the individual level or the roll-up level. See Figure 8.7, on page 65 for a look at how the project appears at a larger scale.

Another thing to note is that the same filter could appear more than once in the rule list if the style of that feature should change dependent on the scale. For example, you may want highways to appear with a wider line at larger scales than at smaller scales.

8.3   Scale in the Print Composer

A nice way to showcase the map in a print layout is to choose some representative scales and add multiple maps to the page, each set to one of the representative scales. Even though the Print Composer is introduced later in the book, you may be interested to know how scale works in a print layout. A short summary is included here.

A print composer named `scales` is in the project file that accompanies this recipe. It shows this map at three scales in a print layout as shown at the beginning of this recipe. In this print composer, we simply added one full-width map to the top third of the page and copied and pasted it two more times, re-positioned the map areas to spread them out on the page, and set their scales to 1:80,000, 1:25,000, and 1:8,000 in the Item properties. With this method three maps are shown with varying scales and varying symbology even though the map in the main QGIS project window has not been altered.

Figure 8.5: The amenities style dialog includes a scale range input

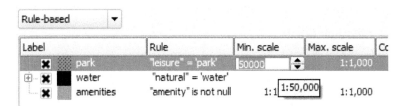

Figure 8.6: Scales can be entered directly in the rules list as well

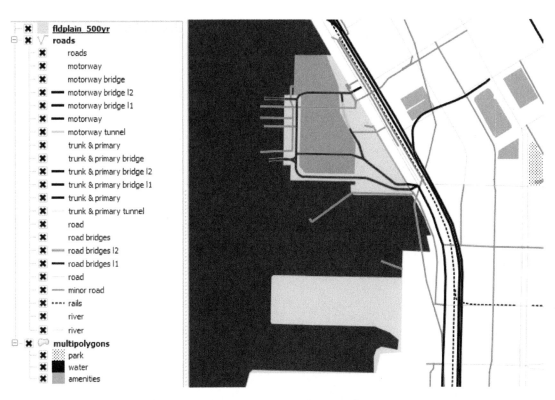

Figure 8.7: The QGIS project with road styling shown at a larger scale

9. Building Blocks for Topographic Maps: Hypsometric Tinting, Hillshade, & Contour Lines

In this recipe, we'll create a classical topographic map featuring hypsometric tints, a hillshade, and contours for the Seattle region. Along the way, we'll explore the wide range of color ramps available in QGIS and how they can be applied to raster layers.

> To reproduce this map in QGIS, open the `hillshade.qgs` project.

9.1 Introducing Hypsometric Tints

Hypsometric tints are colors used to indicate elevation and are usually used together with contour lines to create topographic maps which illustrate the terrain of the land, including valleys and hills. Contour lines (or just "contours") join points of equal elevation (height) at a given level, above or below (often mean) sea level.

Tightly spaced contours thus indicate steep slopes while bigger gaps between contours represent slightly rising or falling terrain. Additionally, hillshades are used to create a three-dimensional effect by drawing shadows on a map which simulate the effect of the sun's rays over the terrain.

9.2 Applying Hypsometric Tints

Elevation data—often in the form of a digital elevation model (DEM)—is a good starting point for a topographic map. The DEM we'll use in this recipe is `seattle_dem_102348.tif`.

To color the elevation layer with hypsometric tints, we use a Singleband pseudocolor renderer. This type of renderer draws the raster layer according to a color map which maps raster cell values to colors. Color maps can be configured manually using the plus and minus buttons to add and delete entries, but in this recipe, we generate the color map automatically using the Generate new color map interface (upper right corner of the Layer Properties | Style section as shown in Figure 9.1). Open the New color ramp ... dropdown list and scroll down to the last entry New color ramp ... to create a new ramp of type cpt-city.

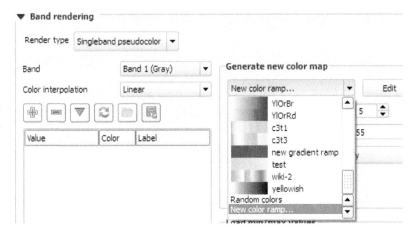

Figure 9.1: Singleband pseudocolor renderer for DEM layer

QGIS comes with a wide range of color ramps to chose from. There is a whole section dedicated to topography and bathymetry color ramps as you can see in Figure 9.2, on the following page. You can see details about a color ramp in the Information tab at the bottom of the dialog. The color ramps were created by different individuals and teams, such as the GRASS Development Team or the UK MET Office, and come in a variety of licenses, including Creative Commons, GPL, BSD-like, and some are in the public domain. In this recipe, we use the public domain wiki-2.0 color ramp, which includes colors for below sea level areas (blue) as well as above sea level (from green to brown and gray).

With a maximum value of 160 meters, our DEM does not contain any particularly high

You can find information about a raster's minimum and maximum values in the Layer Properties | Metadata section.

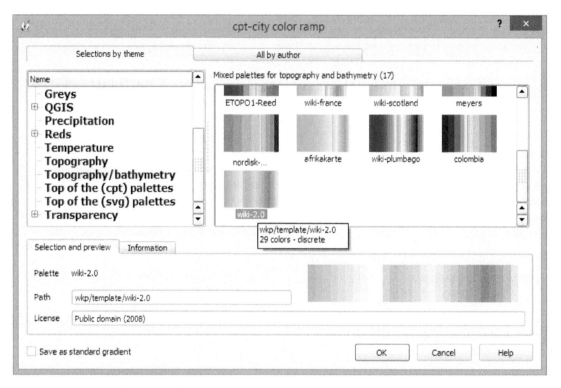

Figure 9.2: cpt-city color ramps dialog

hills or mountains. Therefore, we don't want to use the full range of the color ramp where brown and gray colors usually indicate high elevations in mountainous areas. For this reason, we'll define the Min and Max values manually, setting them to -240 and 500, respectively (see Figure 9.3, on the next page), rather than using the Load min/max values interface which would load the values directly from the DEM. This would result in our small hills being drawn in brown and gray which should be reserved for high mountains.

After pressing the Classify button, the list of colors on the left of the dialog is populated. Using our settings, the border between blue and green shades happens to end up between -10.38 and 15.15. In order to get a nice separation of areas above and below sea level, we can edit the corresponding entries and change -10.38 to 0 and 15.15 to 1. The resulting hypsometric tints looks like Figure 9.4, on the facing page.

9.3   Adding a Hillshade

One way to add a three-dimensional effect to this map is by adding shadows using the `seattle_hillshade_102348.tif` dataset. We style this layer using a Singleband gray renderer set to Black to white between 1 (dark shadow) and 255 (bright sun) as shown in Figure 9.5, on page 70.

In order to combine this hillshade layer with the hypsometric tints below it, we use the Blending mode Overlay. If you test this blending mode with its default settings by pressing Apply, you will notice that the resulting map suffers from rather strong contrasts between light and dark areas. To achieve the desired level of contrast, we reduce the Contrast setting in the Color rendering section to -35. The resulting map combining hillshade and hypsometric tints looks like Figure 9.6, on page 70.

Figure 9.3: Singleband pseudocolor colormap for the DEM layer

Figure 9.4: Hypsometric tinting using the wiki-2
color ramp

lines to emphasize the lightness of this map design.

9.4 Adding Contours

With the basic background map in place, we can add further information by drawing contours (seattle_contours.shp) on top of the raster layers. In this recipe, we limit contours to the land above sea level by applying the Provider feature filter "ELEV" > 0 in the contour layer's General properties.

Figure 9.7, on the next page shows the map with added contours drawn as simple white

The contours were generated from the DEM using the Contour tool in the Raster | Extraction menu.

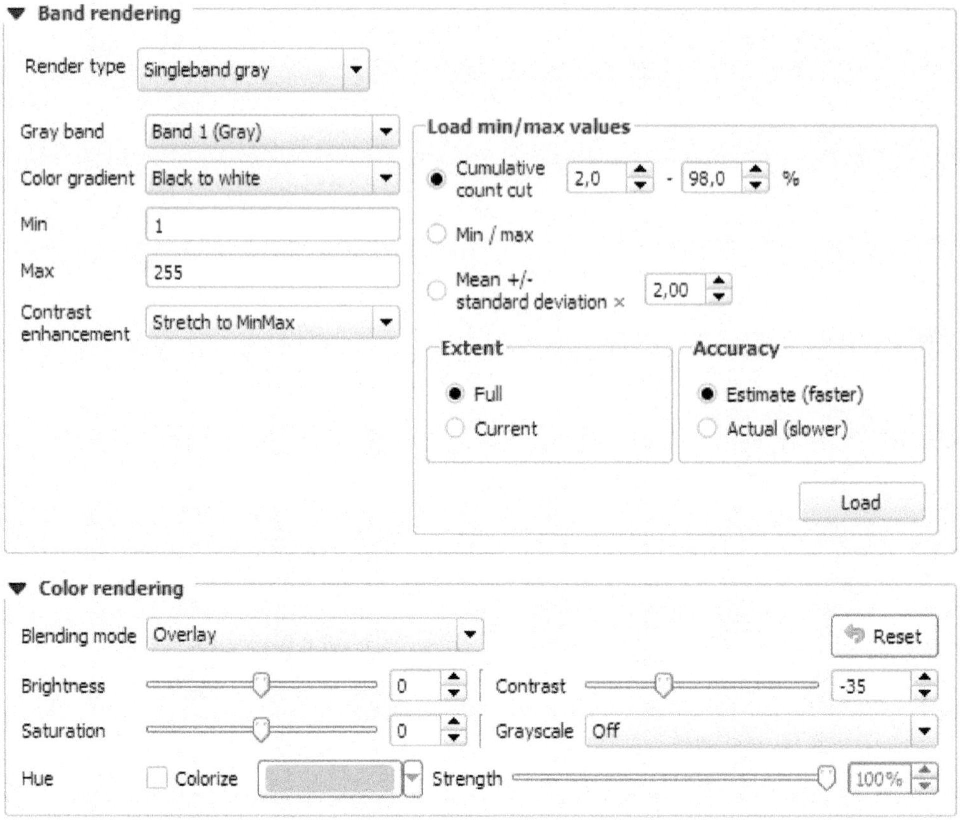

Figure 9.5: Singleband gray renderer for the hillshade layer

9.5   Finishing Touches

To complete this map, we add lakes from our OSM database `seattle_osm.db`. To select the water areas from the multipolygon table, set the Provider feature filter to:

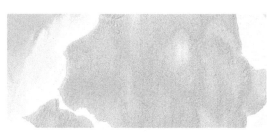

Figure 9.6: Hillshade combined with hypsometric tinting

```
("natural" = 'water' OR
 "other_tags" LIKE '%"water"%' OR
 "other_tags" LIKE '%"waterway"=>"riverbank"%')
AND
"OGC_FID" NOT IN (185330, 185331, 146, 148,
                  16, 147)
```

The first part of the filter ensures that we select all water areas that are tagged with `natural=water`, `water`, or `waterway=riverbank` in OSM. In the second part, the water features we are filtering out based on their `"OGC_FID"` are the water areas below sea level.

Figure 9.7: Added contour lines

The lakes are styled using a **Shapeburst** fill (as introduced in the Shapeburst fill recipe) using the water colors of the hypsometric tinting color map. You can see the final map in Figure 9.8.

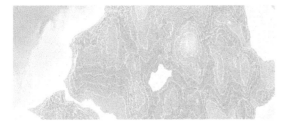

Figure 9.8: Final topographic map with added lake features

10. Styling OSM Roads Like Google Maps

In this recipe, we recreate the Google Maps style using data from OpenStreetMap. We symbolize roads with *cased line symbols* and arrange them in different layers using a rule-based renderer and detailed symbol levels.

> To reproduce this map in QGIS, open the `google_roads.qgs` project.

10.1 Setting Up the First Rules

For this recipe, we'll use data from the SpatiaLite file `seattle_osm.db`. When we load the lines layer from this database, all lines are drawn with the same simple line symbol similar to what is shown in Figure 10.1.

Figure 10.1: All line features drawn with a simple line symbol

To distinguish between the different line types in this recipe, we'll use a Rule-based renderer. On the first level, which is shown in Figure 10.2, we check if a line is a road, rails, or a river.

To add the rules, press the green plus button below the rule list. This opens the **Rule properties** dialog (shown in Figure 10.3) where we

Figure 10.2: The first level of rules

can enter the rule **Label** and **Filter** and pick a symbol for the rule. In the case of the roads rule, we want to further refine the set of rules and it therefore makes little sense to assign a symbol to this first basic rule. That's why we uncheck the **Symbol** checkbox for this rule.

Figure 10.3: Rule properties for the roads base rule

10.2 Adding Detail Rules

When the base rules are ready, we can start adding details. For the roads, we add rules which check the road class as defined by the highway attribute. In this recipe, we want to reproduce the look of Google Maps and therefore we distinguish between four levels of roads from motorways down to minor roads, as shown in Figure 10.4, on the facing page.

The `motorway` rule is the simplest one since it only contains lines with the highway value `'motorway'`

```
"highway" = 'motorway'
```

The second rule labeled `trunk & primary` contains lines which are either `'trunk'`, `'primary'`, or `'motorway_link'`

```
"highway" IN ('motorway_link', 'trunk',
  'primary')
```

If there were bridges with a level higher than 2, we'd have to add further rules.

The same type of rule—using the `IN ()` statement—is used for the third rule labeled `road`

```
"highway" IN ('trunk_link', 'primary_link',
  'secondary', 'secondary_link', 'road',
  'tertiary', 'tertiary_link')
```

The last rule `minor road` contains all other roads by using a `NOT IN ()` statement listing all the previously defined highway values:

```
"highway" NOT IN ('motorway', 'motorway_link',
  'trunk', 'primary', 'trunk_link',
  'primary_link', 'secondary',
  'secondary_link', 'road', 'tertiary',
  'tertiary_link')
```

In order to avoid cluttered maps when zooming out, we introduce two `minor road` rules with different scale limits. This ensures that minor roads are drawn in a very thin line when zoomed out but when we zoom in closer than 1:1000 they will be drawn with a classic road symbol (this same approach is applied to river lines). Note that using these settings, minor roads are only rendered at scales up to 1:125,000.

For the three most important road classes, we furthermore distinguish between bridges (bridge tag in the other_tags attribute):

```
"other_tags" LIKE '%"bridge"=>"yes"%' OR
"other_tags" LIKE '%"bridge"=>"viaduct"%'
```

tunnels (tunnel tag in the other_tags attribute):

```
"other_tags" LIKE '%"tunnel"=>"yes"%'
```

and normal roads on the surface. These third and fourth level rules are shown in Figure 10.5, on the next page.

In this recipe, tunnels are drawn using the same symbol used for roads on the surface but with the Transparency set to 75%. The bridge symbols on the other hand feature an additional symbol level which mimics the shadow dropped by the bridge. Level 1 (`l1`) and level 2 (`l2`) bridge rules are defined to handle the complex situations found at motorway crossings.

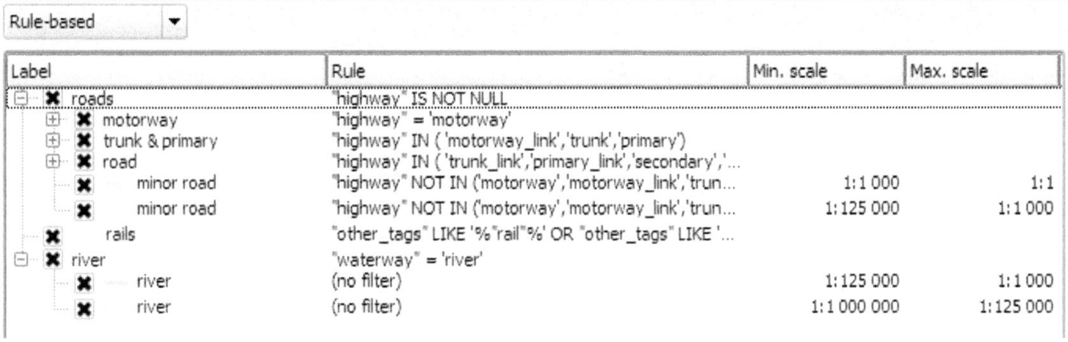

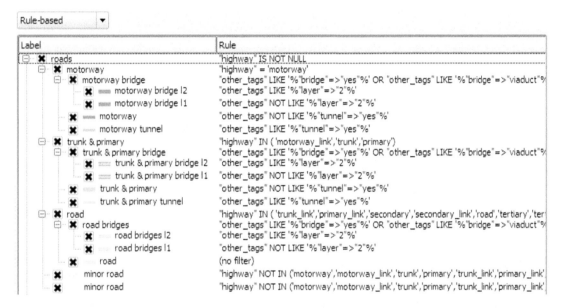

Figure 10.4: Second level of rules for roads, rails, and rivers

Figure 10.5: The complete set of road rules, including bridges and tunnels

10.3 Understanding Road Symbols

Besides the rules, the following settings are key to getting the right look: the correct road symbol settings and a rendering order which ensures the different symbol levels are drawn in the correct order.

To create our road symbols, we use cased line symbols consisting of two symbol layers (three layers for bridges with shadows). Cased line symbols can be created using at least two symbol layers as shown in Figure 10.6, on the following page. The lower layer is a wide and often dark line while the second is a slightly narrower, colored or white line.

In order to make sure the road features look like a connected network, it is important to set the line symbol's Cap style to Flat. Figure 10.7, on the next page shows the effect of default square line caps (left) and flat caps (right).

Finally, to really get the order of bridges, roads and tunnels right, we need to look at the rendering order of our symbol layers. Figure 10.8, on the following page shows a comparison of the road layer without symbol level configuration (on the left) and with correctly configured symbol levels (on the right). As you can see, on the left, it is impossible to tell which roads intersect or connect and which roads are unconnected because they run on different vertical levels.

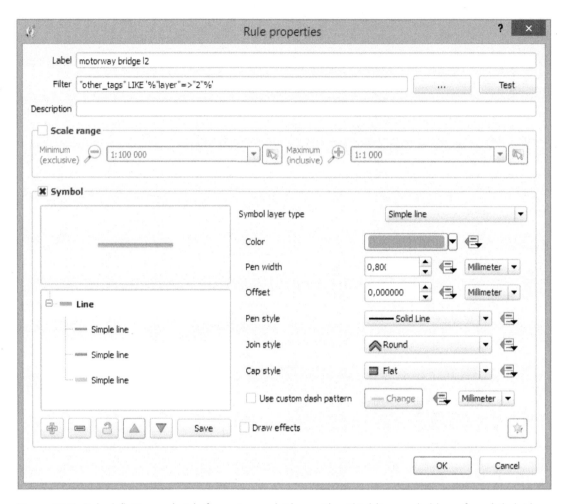

Figure 10.6: Rule definition and style for motorway bridges with a third line symbol layer for subtle bridge shadows

Figure 10.7: Road line symbols with square caps (left) and flat caps (right)

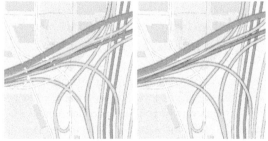

Figure 10.8: Road layer without symbol level configuration (left) and correctly configured levels (right)

You can access this setting using the **Rendering order ...** button below the rule list. Figure 10.9, on the next page shows the rendering order used in this recipe. The lowest value symbol levels will be drawn first. That's why we assign the lowest values (0 and 1) to layers associated with tunnel symbols. These are then followed by river, rail, minor road and road layers (2 and 3). Trunk, primary, and eventually motorway layers follow. Finally, the bridge symbol layers are set to higher values ensuring that bridges are drawn on top while being visually connected to the roads at the ends of the bridge as well as ramps leading up to the bridges.

> We will continue our work on this map in the labeling recipe Data-defined Labeling for Road Maps.

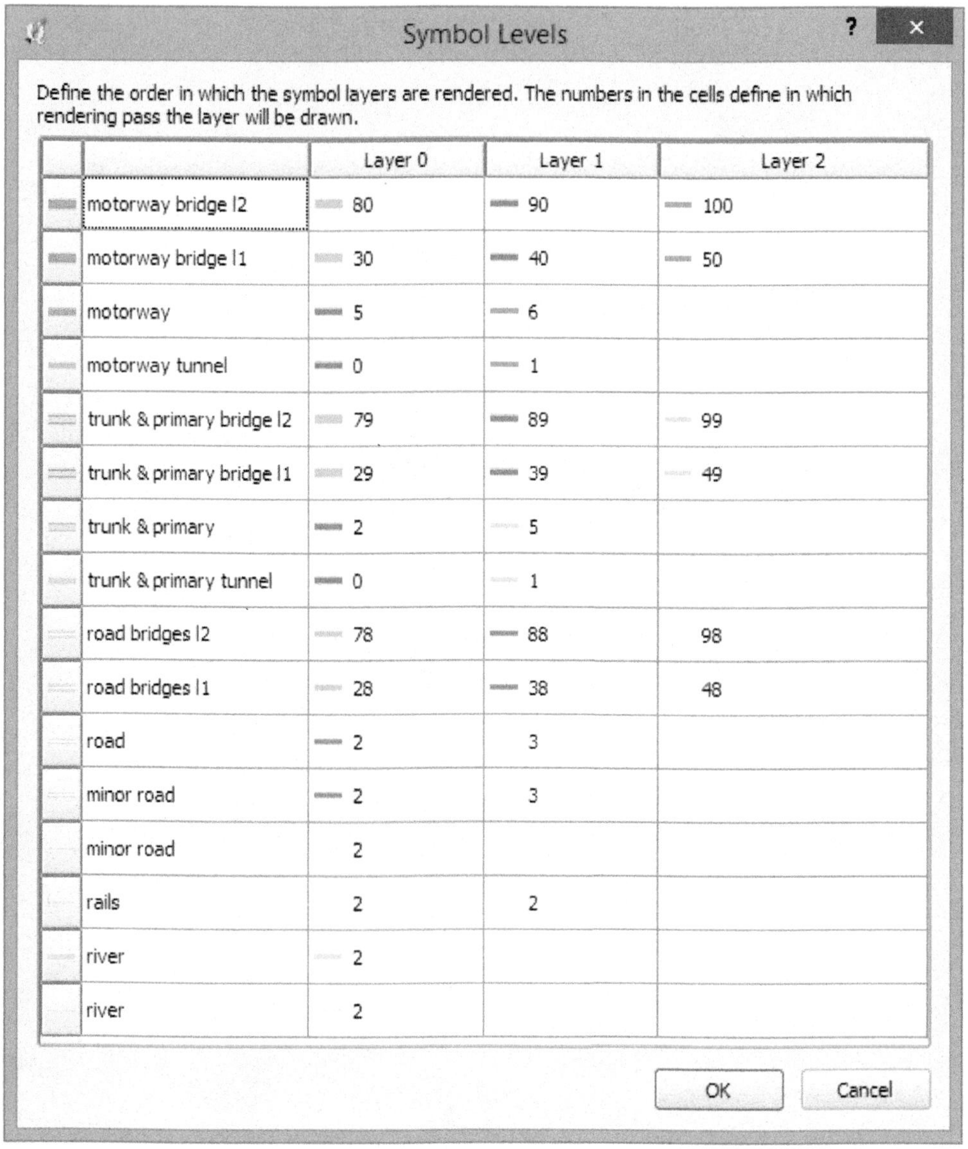

		Layer 0	Layer 1	Layer 2
	motorway bridge l2	80	90	100
	motorway bridge l1	30	40	50
	motorway	5	6	
	motorway tunnel	0	1	
	trunk & primary bridge l2	79	89	99
	trunk & primary bridge l1	29	39	49
	trunk & primary	2	5	
	trunk & primary tunnel	0	1	
	road bridges l2	78	88	98
	road bridges l1	28	38	48
	road	2	3	
	minor road	2	3	
	minor road	2		
	rails	2	2	
	river	2		
	river	2		

Symbol Levels

Define the order in which the symbol layers are rendered. The numbers in the cells define in which rendering pass the layer will be drawn.

[OK] [Cancel]

Figure 10.9: The complete set of symbol levels

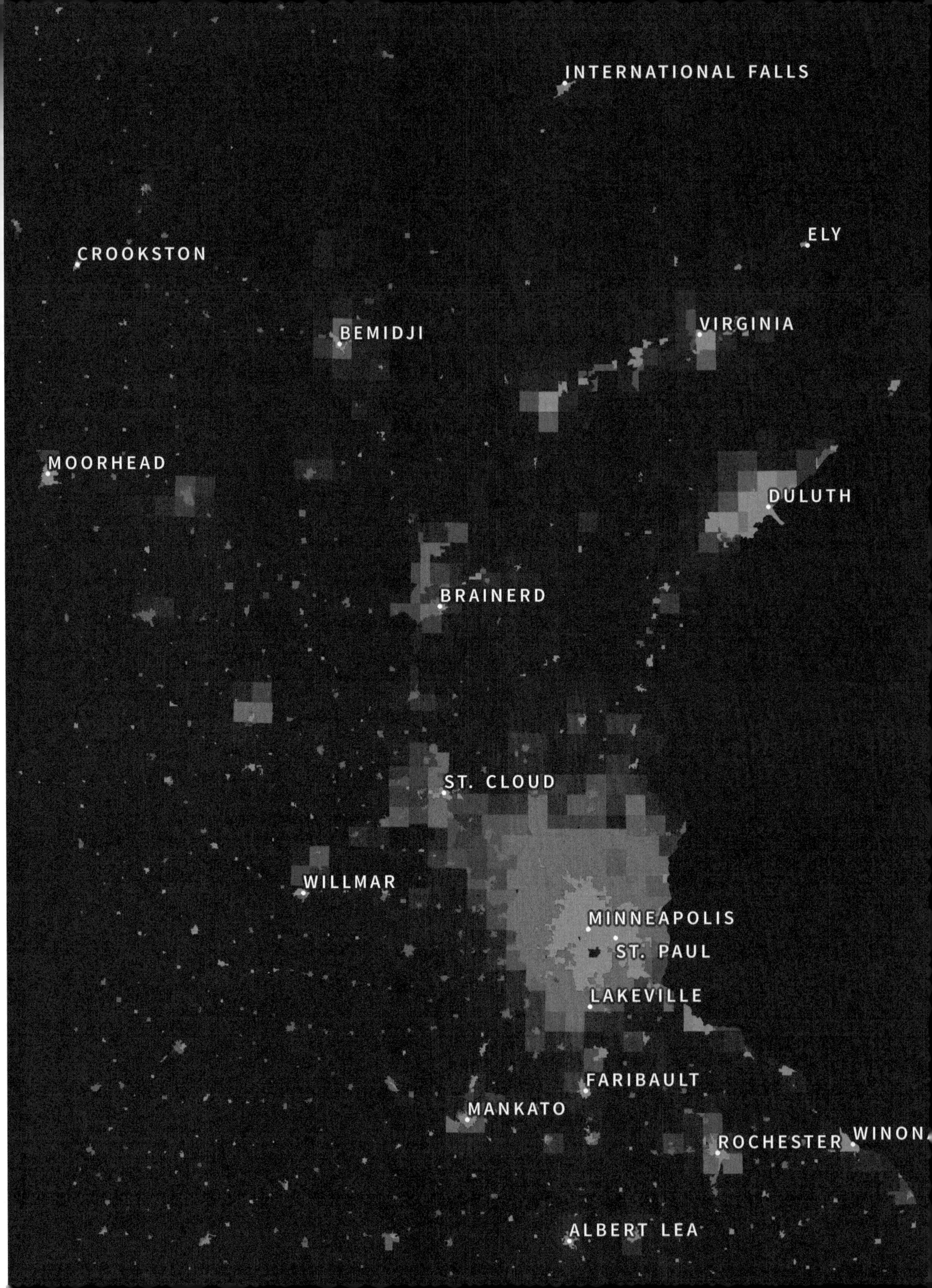
INTERNATIONAL FALLS
ELY
CROOKSTON
BEMIDJI
VIRGINIA
MOORHEAD
DULUTH
BRAINERD
ST. CLOUD
WILLMAR
MINNEAPOLIS
ST. PAUL
LAKEVILLE
FARIBAULT
MANKATO
ROCHESTER
WINON
ALBERT LEA

In this recipe, we create an election map which shows both who won the respective district as well as how many votes were cast in the district. The resulting map puts more emphasis on districts with high populations than on sparsely populated districts.

> To reproduce this map in QGIS, open the electionMN.qgs project.

11.1 Understanding Value by Alpha Mapping

In normal choropleth maps, with a gradient color scheme representing values from low to high, we typically group the data into categories and apply a single color to each category. That method is good when it is important for the map reader to use the legend to determine which color represents which category so that any given place on the map can be matched to a category.

However, if a smoother color scheme is desired and the ability to match locations with their value category isn't important, then another method, called *Value by Alpha*, can be employed. Value by Alpha not only smooths out the data but it also creates a variably transparent scheme for each enumeration unit depending on a second variable.

Value by Alpha mapping was designed as an alternative to cartogram mapping, which uses a second variable to distort the size of the enumeration units. This distorts the map visually and sometimes renders it virtually unusable as a result. In Value by Alpha mapping, the geography remains recognizable in its accurately mapped form while the transparency (aka alpha) is adjusted based on the second variable.

11.2 Creating a Value by Alpha Map

There are multiple ways to achieve Value by Alpha maps in QGIS. In this recipe, we'll follow an approach which does not use a color ramp and thus can be shared easily with other users who might not have the same color ramps configured in their QGIS installation. We simulate the value by alpha effect by overlaying the basic election results with another layer which is black or close to black for sparsely populated districts and transparent for densely populated districts.

We'll use the fact that QGIS evaluates each rule in a Rule-based renderer and if multiple rules apply, the corresponding symbols will be drawn accordingly—one on top of the other. This means that we can have rules taking care of evaluating who won and other rules taking care of the number of voters. In this recipe, we therefore have three rules which check who won (see Figure 11.1): Obama, Romney, or whether they tied.

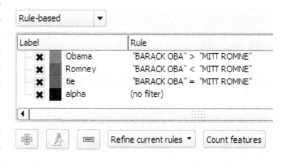

Figure 11.1: Four rules define our Value by Alpha map

Figure 11.2, on the next page shows the map defined by these three rules.

The last rule labeled `alpha` is where Value by Alpha comes into play. This rule has no filter and that means it will apply to all features in our layer.

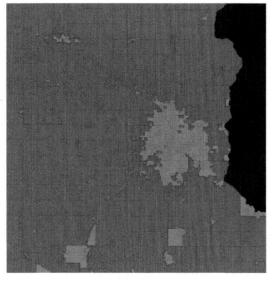

RGB is a familiar color model that separates the red, green, and blue components of a color into numbers from 0 to 255. Thus, each color is represented by a triplet of numbers. For example, 255,0,0 is red. *RGBA* brings another dimension to the RGB color model by providing an additional number - also between 0 and 255 - that indicates the transparency of the color. For example, 255,0,0,255 is full red while 255,0,0,125 is semi-transparent red. This additional number is referred to as the "alpha".

Figure 11.2: Basic map without alpha overlay

To ensure that the alpha symbol will be drawn on top of the other symbols, we define the rendering order as shown in Figure 11.3. Press the Rendering order ... button below the rule list to access the Symbol Levels dialog.

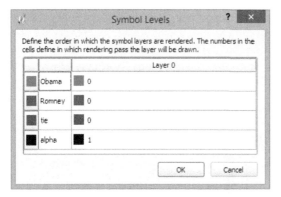

Figure 11.3: Ensure that the alpha layer is drawn on top of all other symbol layers

Our goal for the alpha layer is to draw a district in black or near black color if it is home to very few voters and, in the opposite case, if a district is home to many voters, it should be drawn in bright colors. Figure 11.4, on the next page shows how to achieve this effect by configuring a data-defined override for the symbol color.

Pressing the override button next to the Fill color and selecting Edit ... opens the Expression string builder. Here we can enter the expression to define the symbol fill color. In this recipe,

we use the `color_rgba()` function. You can access the documentation of any function by selecting it from the function list in the center of the dialog as shown in Figure 11.5, on the facing page.

The expression we use is:

```
color_rgba( 0,0,0,
  scale_linear( "Total Resu"/($area/10000000),
  0,250,
  255,0))
```

On the first line, we define the red, green, and blue components as 0 which results in black. On the remaining three lines, we use the `scale_linear()` function to map the voter density

```
"Total Resu"/($area/10000000)
```

to an alpha value between 255 (opaque black) to 0 (completely transparent). This means that a voter density of 0 will result in a completely black fill while a density of 250 or higher will result in a completely transparent fill which will let the underlying color of the winning candidate shine through.

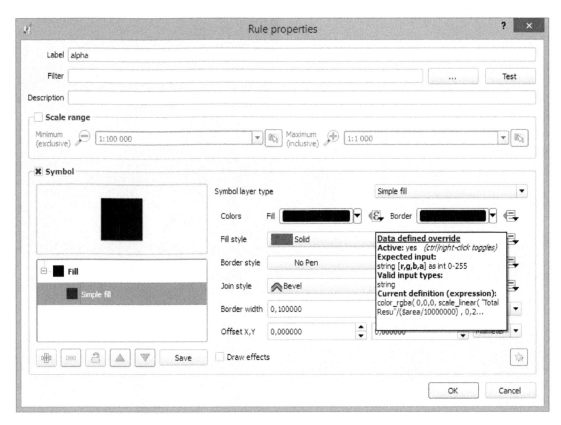

Figure 11.4: The alpha symbol uses a data-defined color override

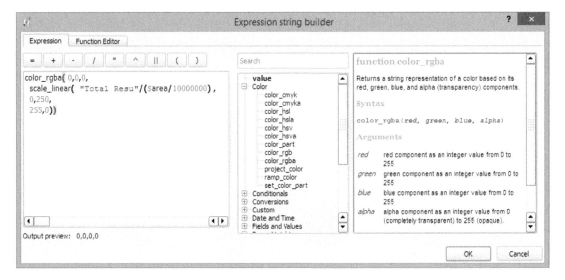

Figure 11.5: This expression defines the alpha value based on voter density

11.3 Creating a Value by Alpha Map

The final map is shown in Figure 11.6. On the full page map at the beginning of this recipe, we've used the ne_10m_populated_places.shp dataset to add additional information in the form of place names. For more details about labeling, please refer to the next part of the book, which is dedicated to labeling recipes.

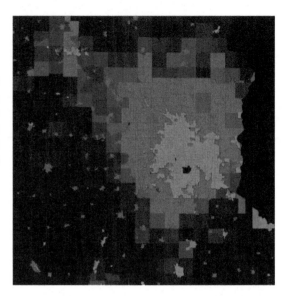

Figure 11.6: Final map with voter density defining fill color alpha

12. Visualizing Global Connections

In this recipe, we'll create a map of a hemisphere of the globe in an azimuthal orthographic projection. Our map shows connections between New York City (NYC) and its sister cities as listed on Wikipedia[16]: Santo Domingo, Cairo, Brasília, Madrid, Budapest, Jerusalem, London, Rome, Johannesburg, Tokyo, and Beijing.

> To reproduce this map in QGIS, open the global_connections.qgs project.

12.1 Preparing the Background Map Data

Using on the fly reprojection with an azimuthal orthographic projection can be messy and full of artifacts. To get good results, it's helpful to clip the input data to the desired hemisphere before reprojecting. Luckily there is a plugin for that—we'll use the **Clip to Hemisphere** plugin[17] which adds a tool called **Clip a vector layer to the hemisphere centered on a user specified point** to the Processing Toolbox as shown in Figure 12.1.

In this recipe, we want to center our map on Rome, which is located at 42.1 degrees latitude and 12.8 degrees longitude (this way we can show all cities, and eventually, all roads lead to Rome anyway). We specify this center location in the clip tool as shown in Figure 12.2, on the next page and clip the countries layer.

In addition, we need to create a disk to represent the ocean areas. To this end, we create a rectangle covering the maximum valid latitude/longitude extent using:*

```
Polygon((-180 90, 180 90, 180 -90, -180 -90,
    -180 90))
```

and clip it to our desired hemisphere as well.

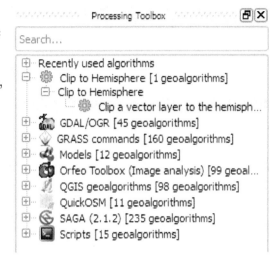

Figure 12.1: The Clip to Hemisphere plugin adds a tool to the Processing Toolbox

Figure 12.3, on the following page shows the resulting clipped layers in color on top of the black and white input layers.

Once the layers are clipped, we can reproject them using the following custom orthographic projection centered on Rome:

```
+proj=ortho +lat_0=42.1 +lon_0=12.8 +x_0=0
+y_0=0 +a=6371000 +b=6371000 +units=m
+no_defs
```

Figure 12.4, on the next page shows the resulting map.

> For instructions on creating user-defined projections in QGIS, see the QGIS user manual (http://loc8.cc/qmd/proj).

> *You can copy and paste the WKT definition for the rectangular polygon into an empty polygon layer to create the feature—make sure the WKT is all on one line.

16. http://loc8.cc/qmd/nyc_sisters
17. http://loc8.cc/qmd/clip_to_hemisphere

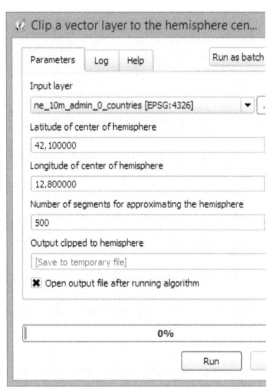

Figure 12.2: Clip the countries and the background layer

Figure 12.4: Reproject the clipped layers using our custom azimuthal orthographic projection

12.2 Styling the Hemisphere

To recreate this map, we need two copies of the hemisphere disk layer. One is styled using a normal **Single Symbol** renderer with **Shapeburst** fill as shown in Figure 12.5, on the facing page. This fills the hemisphere with a gradient which is dark blue (#1f3d52) at the border and medium blue (#366485) in the center.

The second copy is used to style the space around our hemisphere disk and add a nice halo effect. To achieve this effect, we use an **Inverted polygons** renderer as shown in Figure 12.6, on the next page. The gradient used for the **Shapeburst** fill transitions from light blue (#9fdaf1) to black (#000000).

Finally, we style the country layer in a transparent white. Figure 12.7, on page 88 shows the resulting map.

12.3 Adding Connections

Finally, we will add the connections between New York and its sister cities. This kind of visualization looks much nicer if the connections are curved instead of simple straight lines. Of course, we could draw the curved connecting lines by hand but there are ways to automate this.

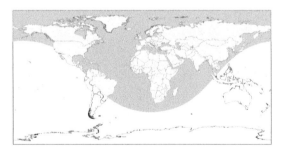

Figure 12.3: When the layers are clipped we can then reproject them

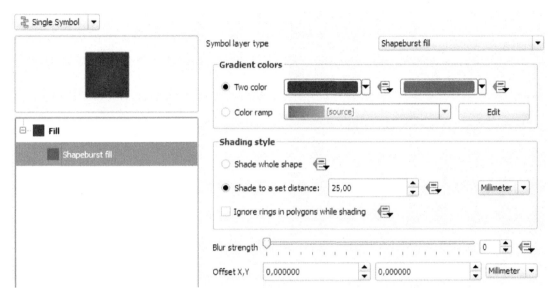

Figure 12.5: This shapeburst fill creates a pseudo 3D effect for our globe

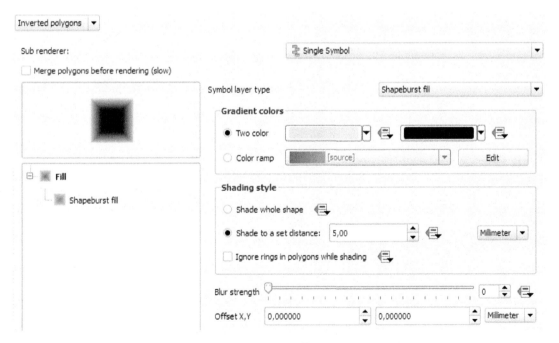

Figure 12.6: This inverted shapeburst fill creates a halo effect around the globe

Figure 12.7: Style the hemisphere using shapeburst fill symbols to create pseudo 3D and halo effects

One approach is described in Anita Graser's *Visualizing global connections* blog post[18]. To recreate in QGIS, start with simple straight lines connecting the cities in WGS84 EPSG:4326 (green lines in Figure 12.8).

Figure 12.8: Creating curved connection lines is all about additional vertices and projections

To make the lines curve, we need to insert additional vertices using the Densify geometries tool from the Processing Toolbox. If we just densify the lines in WGS84 we end up with the orange lines. They are curved but certainly not

the most direct connections possible. To get nice direct connections, we reproject the lines to Sphere Equidistant Conic EPSG:53027 before densifying them as shown in Figure 12.9. This creates the pink lines. You will notice some artifacts at the north pole. These have to be fixed manually.

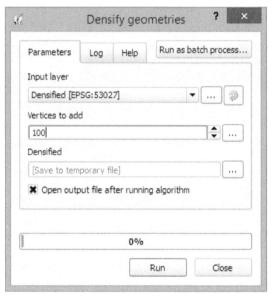

Figure 12.9: Densify the reprojected lines to make them curve

With the curved connections in place, we only need to style them using wide, semi-transparent white lines. To add context to the map, we also label the cities. For more details about labeling, please refer to the following part.

18. http://loc8.cc/qmd/global

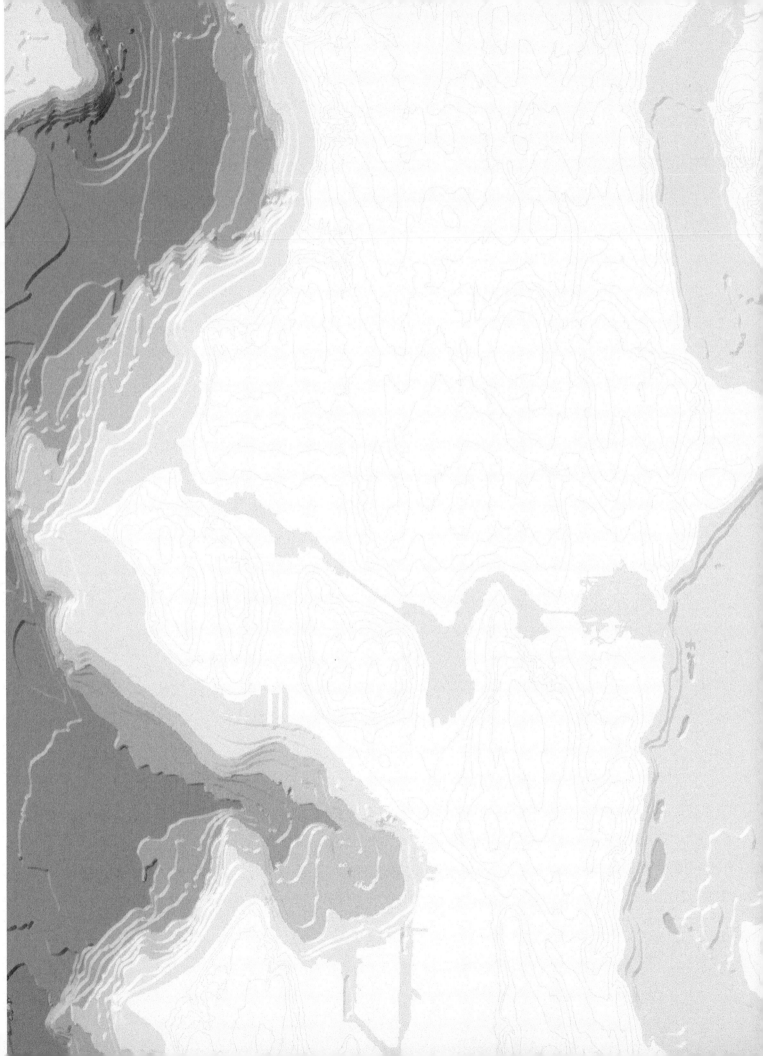

13. Illuminated Contours Tanaka-Style

In this recipe, we take the concept of contour lines to a new level by creating illuminated contours, also known as Tanaka contours. Along the way, we will explore how automated data processing workflows, such as the automatic generation of Tanaka contours, can be used for cartographic purposes.

> To reproduce this map in QGIS, open the tanaka.qgs project.

13.1 Understanding Illuminated/Tanaka Contours

Tanaka contours are a method of displaying terrain developed by Prof. Tanaka Kitiro in 1950. This method applies a light source (typically positioned in the northwest) to a contour map. The method involves changing the width and color of contour lines based on their relationship to the light source. Contour lines facing the light source are drawn in white while those in the shadow are drawn in black. Lines perpendicular to the light source are drawn thinner. The result is a 3D-like representation that gives a realistic shadow-effect that allows the reader to understand the features of the landscape more easily.

13.2 Preprocessing the Contours

In "How to create illuminated contours, Tanaka-style"[19], Anita Graser describes the basic steps to create Tanaka contours from a DEM. In this recipe, we'll use a more refined approach which you can easily reproduce by running the Processing model (Figure 13.1) found in the resources folder. All you need to recreate this effect is a DEM. The DEM we'll use in this recipe is `seattle_dem_102348.tif`.

The model uses a custom function to compute the line orientation called `azimuth()`. Figure 13.2 shows this function in the **Function Editor**.

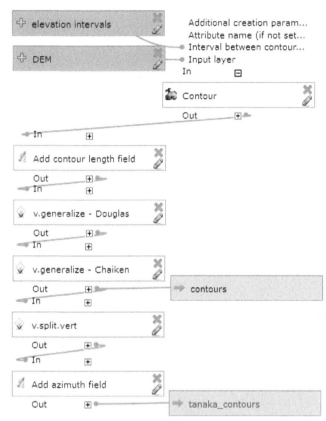

Figure 13.1: This model creates Tanaka contours from an input DEM

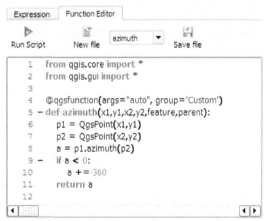

Figure 13.2: User-defined function to compute the azimuth

If you want to go straight to the styling, you can skip the data preprocessing step and load the `seattle_contours_tanaka.shp` file in the sample data.

19. `http://loc8.cc/qmd/tanaka`

91

The model implements a number of steps. First, GDAL **Contour** is used to create contour lines at specified intervals from the DEM. Then, the model adds a field with the contour length which we will use later in this recipe. Next, it applies **Douglas** and **Chaiken** algorithms to simplify and smooth the contour lines. After this step, the first output—nicely generalized contour lines—is generated.

In order to be able control the brightness of the illuminated contours, we need to compute the orientation of every subsection of the contours. To accomplish this, the next step in the model splits the contour lines at each node using `v.split.vert`. Figure 13.3 shows the split contours drawn with arrows. We can see that they all wrap around the mountain in clockwise direction (light DEM cells equal higher elevation).

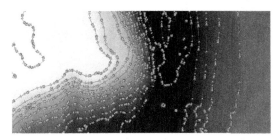

Figure 13.3: Contours created with GDAL wrap around mountains in clockwise direction

Finally, the model computes the orientation of each subsection of the contours and writes it in the newly created azimuth field.

13.3   Styling Illuminated Contours

Using the line orientation stored in the azimuth field, we can now write an expression that controls the contour line color. For example, if we want the sun to appear in the north west (-45°) we can use the expression shown in Figure 13.4 to configure the data-defined line color. This expression will draw the lines which are directly exposed to the sun white by setting the lightness to the highest possible value of **100**, while the lines in the shadows will be black with lightness set to **0**.

Another important aspect of Tanaka's method

```
Expression     Function Editor

 =    +    -    /    *    ^    ||   (   )

set_color_part (
 'black',
 'lightness',
 scale_linear( abs(
  (CASE WHEN "azimuth"-45 < 0
        THEN "azimuth"-45+360
        ELSE "azimuth"-45 END) -180 ),
  0,180,
  0,100)
)
```

Output preview: 168,168,168,255

Figure 13.4: Expression that defines the contour color based on the line's azimuth

is to also alter the contour line width. Lines in the sun or shadow should be wider (1 in this example) than those in orthogonal direction (0.2 in this example):

```
scale_linear( abs(
  (CASE WHEN "azimuth"-45 < 0
        THEN "azimuth"-45+360
        ELSE "azimuth"-45 END) -180 ) -90),
  0,90,
  0.2,1)
```

Figure 13.5 shows the resulting map

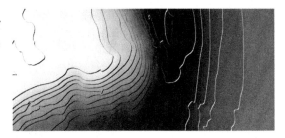

Figure 13.5: Basic illuminated contours on default singleband gray DEM

To achieve a more subtle effect, we use the **Overlay** layer blending mode to blend contours and DEM color. The result is shown in Figure 13.6, on the facing page.

The final step, is to style the DEM. We want to create the effect of discrete elevation classes instead of a smooth color gradient. Therefore, we change the DEM layer's **Render type** to **Singleband pseudocolor**. Since we only want to style

Figure 13.6: Tanaka contours on default singleband gray DEM

the areas below water, we create a color map which only covers negative values as shown in Figure 13.7.

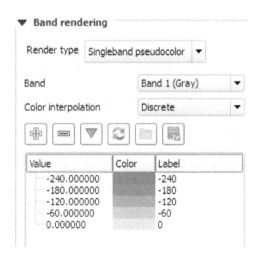

Figure 13.7: Use discrete color interpolation for the DEM

Figure 13.8 shows a section of resulting map with discrete elevation classes. The effect of discrete elevation classes can easily be achieved by changing the color interpolation mode of the DEM from Linear to Discrete.

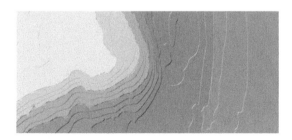

Figure 13.8: Tanaka contours on colored DEM

13.4 Finishing Touches

As you can see from the map at the beginning of this recipe, we use a different, much simpler, contour style for the land area. This provides the added effect of drawing the reader's attention to the water areas. The Tanaka contours use the filter:

```
"ELEV" < 0 and "length" > 1000
```

while the land contours are limited to:

```
"ELEV" > 0 and "length" > 1000
```

In both cases, we discard contours which are less than 1,000 meters in order to avoid unnecessary visual clutter on our map. Figure 13.9 provides a comparison of the effect of unfiltered contours (left) versus the cleaner results achieved by removing short contours (right).

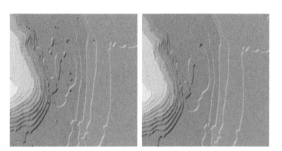

Figure 13.9: Map with all contour features (left) and result if short contour lines are eliminated (right)

The color inspiration for this map comes from aerial images found on http://loc8.cc/qmd/reef.

Part 2

Labeling

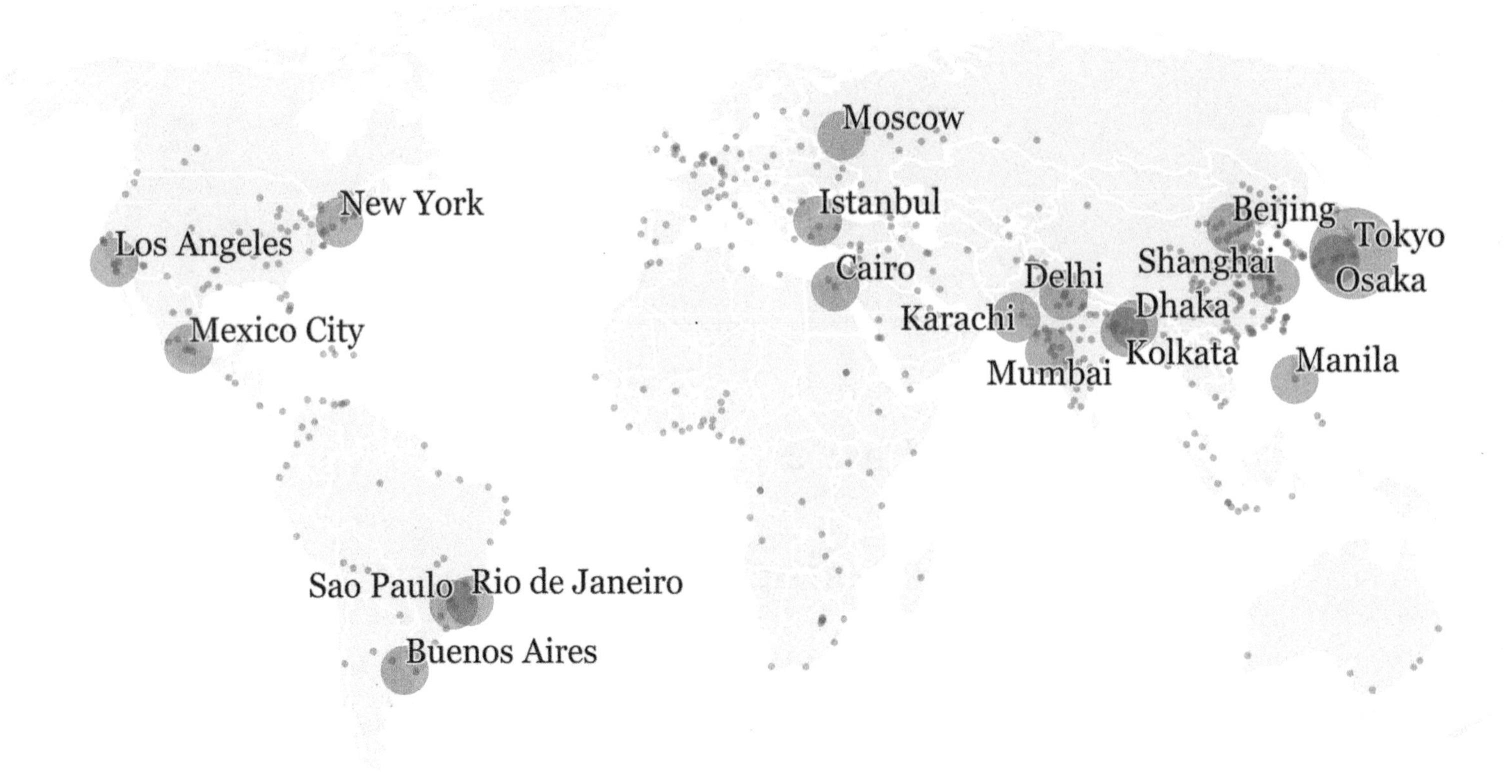

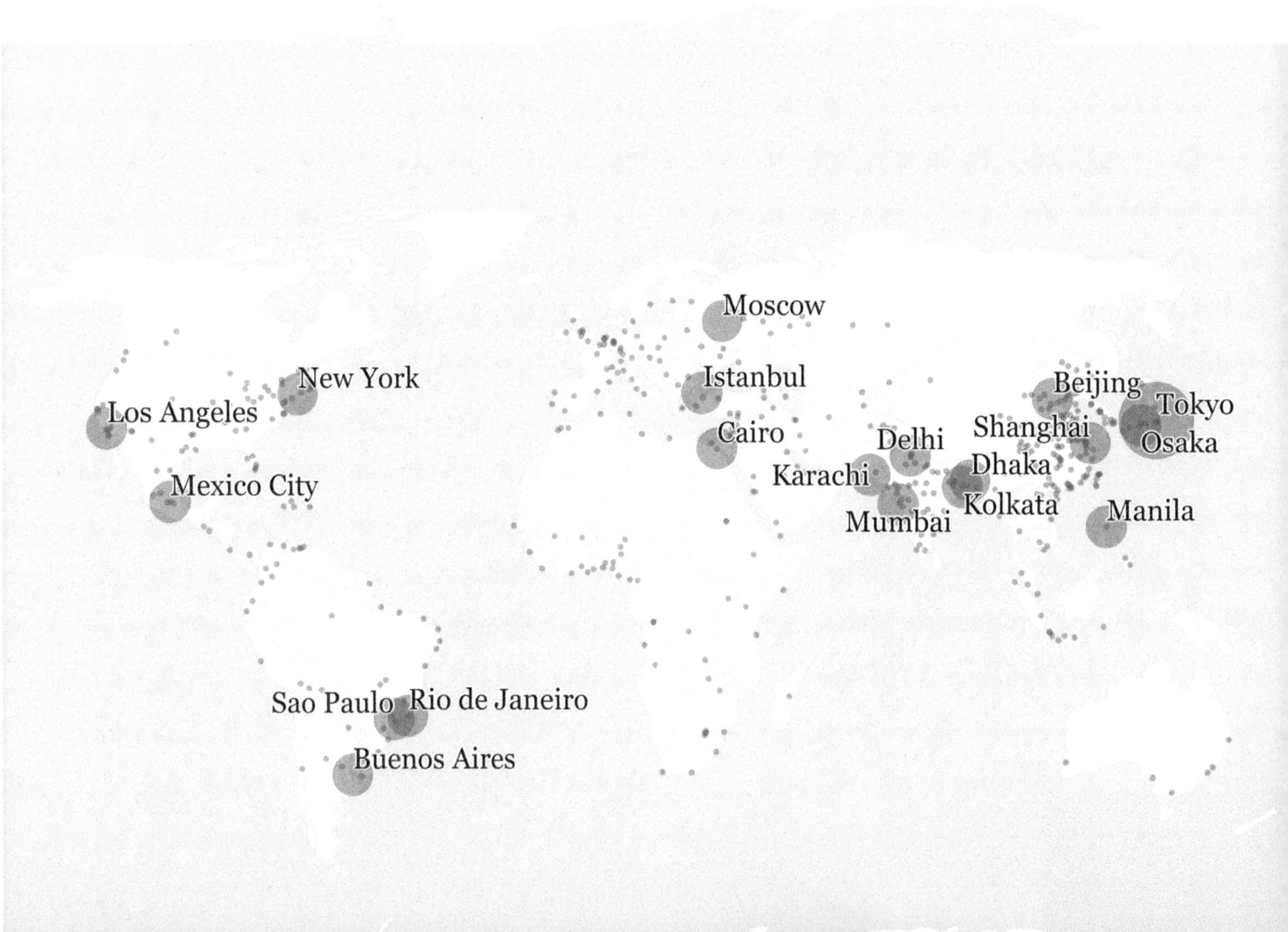

In this recipe we take the map created in Graduated Symbol Sizes, on page 19 and label the metropolitan centers with populations greater than 10 million.

> To reproduce this map in QGIS, begin with the finished map from the Graduated Symbol Sizes recipe, which can be found in the graduated_symbol_sizes.qgs project. Alternatively, view this finished recipe in the restricted_labeling.qgs project.

1.1 Setting Up the Labels

Before beginning, you'll want to make sure to remember that the units in the metropolitan population legend are in the millions by renaming the ne_10m_populated_places layer to: Metro Population in Millions.

To automatically display labels on features in QGIS, such as names of places, heights of mountains, or identification numbers, simply open the Layer Properties, Labels section and change the first drop-down to Show labels for this layer as shown in Figure 1.1, on the next page. Then choose the field in the data that contains the names, heights, identification numbers, or whatever it is that you want to label. Do this for the metro population layer and use NAME as the label field.

In the Text sub-menu change the Font to Georgia, size 13.† Georgia is a fairly common font available as a core Microsoft Windows font and Apple iOS font. It's also available in the Linux msttcorefonts package. The terms font and typeface are used synonymously in this book.

The labels will stand out more if we create a subtle buffer or halo around the text, which will serve to visually break the background features before they come into contact with the letter forms. This kind of unobtrusive buffer technique is commonly employed to help ensure that the label text doesn't have multiple

colors or lines running underneath it and is typically designed such that the buffer color is the same hue as the dominant background hue of the map. If we were to use a highlighter color such as bright yellow or blue, instead of the background color, the buffers would have more impact than warranted in this map.

In the Buffer sub-menu, ensure that the Draw text buffer checkbox is checked, keep the size of the buffer at 0.5 millimeter, and change the color to match the gray countries. Applying the changes at this state results in a map that appears a little bit too cluttered* as shown in Figure 1.2, on the following page.

*Understatement

The map will look better if only the largest population centers are labeled. In the Layer Properties, Labels, Rendering sub-menu scroll down to the Data defined section and make sure that Show all labels for this layer (including colliding labels) is checked, then click the Expression button next to Show label and click Edit... as shown in Figure 1.3, on the next page.

Type the following expression in the Expression string builder window:

```
"POP_MAX" >= 10000000
```

The Expression button now turns yellow to indicate that it is active. As you try out different labeling expressions on other maps, you may wish to deactivate an expression and it is good to note that when you do this, the GUI will retain the previously used expression in case you'd like to activate it again. Apply the change to the map and note that now only those population centers with a population of more than 10 million are labeled.

†Click the drop-down menu for the Font and then type a G in order to auto-scroll to the fonts that begin with G.

The final map is shown, along with an inverted color scheme, at the beginning of this recipe.

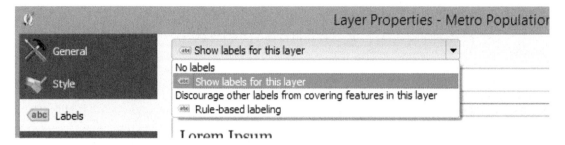

Figure 1.1: Show labels for this layer

Figure 1.2: There are too many labels

Figure 1.3: The data defined expression button

In this recipe we'll continue refining the coffee map from the Custom SVGs recipe by adding handwriting inspired labels to the map that have added visibility through the use of text buffering. Text buffers are sometimes referred to as halos.

In this recipe we'll be careful to make sure the buffer size and color are appropriate so that the buffer doesn't detract from the main typeface character. Remember that typeface designers work on each individual character to achieve a certain look, and when we add buffers or halos this unique look and feel is altered—usually for the worst. Therefore, it's usually best to create text buffers that are as thin and subtly hued as possible.

> To reproduce this map in QGIS, open the `text_buffers.qgs` project or begin with the finished map from `custom_svgs.qgs` and build up from there.

2.1 Installing a Typeface

It seems that cartographers are always experimenting with new typefaces. Here we'll install a new typeface that has the coffee shop vibe we're after. To begin, locate the typeface file `breve-sc.zip` in the resources folder, unzip it, and install the font onto your machine. Alternatively, use the typeface of your choice, keeping in mind that we're looking for a hand-drawn feel for this map. For Windows font install instructions see Microsoft's Install or Uninstall Fonts documentation. For iOS font install instructions see the Apple support pages. Once the font is installed on your operating system, restart QGIS if it was open during the install process. Your new font should now be recognized by QGIS.

2.2 Adding Labels to the Coffee Shops

Using the Layer properties, Labels sub-menu, choose Show labels for this layer, labeling them with the name field. In the Text sub-menu, change the font to Breve SC (or to whichever font you've decided to use), which should now be in the font list as per the above installation process. Change the size to 18.

We recommend using the Apply button frequently in order to gain instant visual feedback on label changes without closing the Layer Properties window.

Because our large coffee mug icon takes up a lot of space around the points, it's necessary to offset the labels such that they don't overlap with the icons. To do this, set the Placement, Around point to 4 millimeters as shown in Figure 2.1.

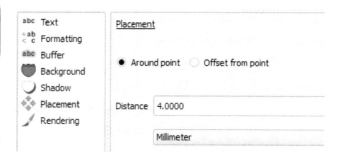

Figure 2.1: Placing labels a little farther away from the point centroid to accommodate large icons

Now we'll try a text buffer with the defaults. In the Buffer sub-menu, check the box next to Draw text buffer. Notice that the default text buffer is white, with a size of 1. This makes the labels much more visible on the map, but also provides undue visual emphasis and a garish appearance as shown in Figure 2.2, on the next page.

To remedy this, set the color of the buffer to the same color as the main background color (the land), and increase the buffer size to 2. See Figure 2.3, on the following page for a comparison between non-buffered text and subtly buffered text.

Figure 2.2: Default buffer options are too prominent and garish here

Figure 2.3: A label without a buffer (left) compared with a land colored buffer (right)

Now the labels are highly readable yet maintain equal visual emphasis with the icons. Note that an alternate method of masking underlying features is possible with the Layer properties, Background, Rectangle tool. However this method may create a more blocky masking effect than intended.

2.3   Adding Labels to the Roads

To add labels to the roads (lines) layer, enable them for the layer in the same way as above, labeling them by the name field. We also want to abbreviate road names that include "Street." To do this, use the following expression in the Layer Properties, Labels, Label with box:

```
replace(name, 'Street', 'St.')
```

Change the text color to something a bit darker than the land, but still within the same hue. In our recipe we've used **#996b3b**. For the font, use Arial, size 8.25. Applying these changes lets us see that there are probably too many duplicate road labels on the map, as shown in Figure 2.4.

To declutter the labels, use the Layer Properties, Labels, Rendering, Feature options, Merge connected lines to avoid duplicate labels option. Since road features are commonly comprised of separate lines for each city block, on-the-fly merging is important for this layer. This tool

Scale terms are often misinterpreted. "Smaller scale" means smaller features. In other words, more zoomed out.

Figure 2.4: Feature parts are each labeled individually even though they represent the same street

makes it so the cartographer doesn't have to create a separate merged feature dataset solely for labeling purposes.

In the Placement sub-menu, change the priority slider so that it is set to Low (the priority slider is found at the bottom of the Placement sub-menu). See the result of these changes in Figure 2.5. Depending on the purpose of your map, its final output scale, and the aesthetic being aimed for, you may or may not want to further adjust these settings.

Figure 2.5: Using the merge features label option decreases label density

At this point, you'll notice that the map has some labels that protrude into the Puget Sound water area as shown in Figure 2.6, on the next page.

The land colored buffers on these labels may erroneously be mistaken for land or piers. In many cases this may be perfectly acceptable, especially for maps with hundreds or thousands of labels depicted at a smaller scale.* However, for this map it would be better to try and constrain the labels such that they appear only over the land.

To force the labels to render only over the land features, we need to adjust a few things in the coffee points layer. First, change the label from

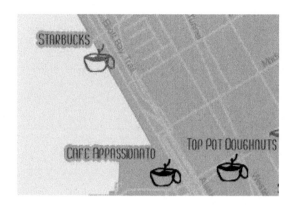

Figure 2.6: Labels are jutting into the water features

name to `wordwrap(name,18)`. This automatically creates multiline labels for coffee shops with long names using 18 as the ideal number of characters that a line should contain. Also set the priority slider to high. Now, change the label properties of the multipolygons layer (i.e., water layer) so that the first drop-down reads `Discourage other labels from covering features in this layer.`

The labels are now optimized as shown in Figure 2.7.

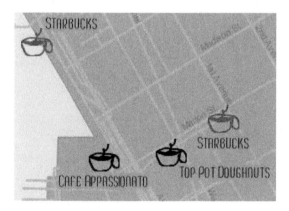

Figure 2.7: Labels now appear only over the land features

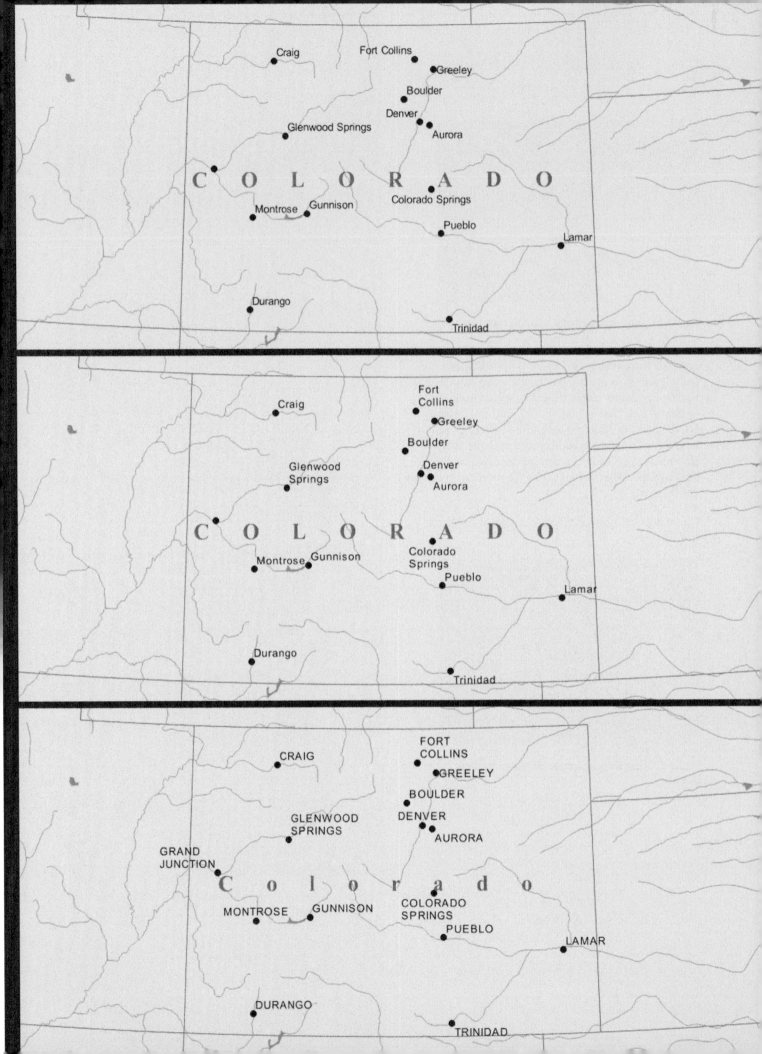

3. Typecase and Letter Spacing for Label Hierarchies

Maps with many labeled layers, or with many varying labels within a single layer, need prominent label hierarchies. The three exercises presented in this chapter illustrate how to create simple hierarchies and how to manage the visual consequences of large lettering.

> To reproduce this map in QGIS, open the typecase_and_letter_spacing.qgs project.

3.1 Setting Up the Basemap

The labels for all three exercises are displayed on the same simple basemap map of Colorado. To create the basemap, add the:

ne_10m_admin_1_states_provinces

shapefile to a new project. Change the style to a simple fill with #7acd22 (green) fill and a #6d5455 (brown) border.

There are three layers for the water features on the map. Add:

ne_10m_rivers_lake_centerlines
ne_10m_rivers_north_america

to the map and change their color to #166cc8 (blue). Also add:

ne_10m_lakes_north_america

and use the same blue color for its fill, no border.

Change the CRS for the project to EPSG:102653, NAD 1983 State Plane Colorado North Feet, then zoom to the state of Colorado.

3.2 Exercise 1: Expanding the Colorado Label

A common mapping typography technique is to widen letter spacings for large area labels. For example, a mountain range can be labeled along its length, or a large country can be labeled across its width. With wide letter spacing, however, the risk is that labels can become less readable.

In this first example, we want to indicate that the label for the state of Colorado is important, but we also don't want it to dominate the city labels. Therefore, we'll use a bold, serif, uppercase font for the label, but minimize its impact by using a medium brown for the text color instead of the default black.

Open the Layer Properties, Labels sub-menu for the states layer, choose Show labels for this layer in the drop-down, label with the name field, Times New Roman font (this is a serif style font), bold, size 20 pt, color 6d5455, typecase All uppercase, and spacing 30 as shown in Figure 3.1, on the next page.

If desired, make it so that only the Colorado state label appears and not the labels for the surrounding states by using the Layer Properties, Labels, Rendering sub-menu. Under Data defined, Show label there is an expression button. Click it, go to Edit and enter the following in the Expression string builder:

"name" = 'Colorado'

Now, add the ne_10m_populated_places shapefile to the map. In the layer properties, use the following Provider feature filter expression:

"ADM1NAME" = 'Colorado'

This constrains the populated places points to Colorado. For the populated places labels, use

Use data defined overrides for restricted labels while still showing all features and use provider feature filters for restricting the entire layer, both features and their labels.

105

Figure 3.1: Increasing the spacing to 30 allows the label to span the width of Colorado

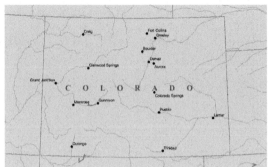

Figure 3.3: Changing the Colorado label to brown lowers its visual prominence while still maintaining a "stately" presence with uppercase, widely spaced letters.

the NAME field, the Arial font (this is a sans-serif style font), size 10 pt, black, and placement distance 1. We've styled the points as circles with black fill and a size of 2.

Figure 3.2 shows the map with a black Colorado label while Figure 3.3 shows the map with the more subdued medium brown Colorado label.

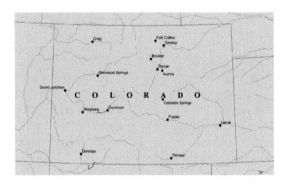

Figure 3.2: The black Colorado label is competitive with the populated places labels

3.3   Exercise 2: Styling the City Labels

To add extra heft to the city labels, a small increase in letter spacing will help. Change the populated places layer properties so that the

spacing is set to 1. With even this small increase in letter spacing it will be necessary to wrap multiword city names. Do this by changing the layer properties so that the **Formatting, Wrap-on character** box has a space in it (i.e., tap the space bar once inside the box) as shown in Figure 3.4.

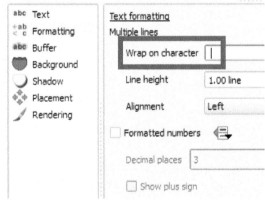

Figure 3.4: Using a space as a word wrap indicator

The finished map for this exercise now has more prominent city labels as shown in the final map, Figure 3.5, on the next page.

3.4   Exercise 3: Deemphasizing the State Label

If a further deemphasis of the state label is required, it could be changed to a mixed case label style and the populated places could be changed to an uppercase style. This is done by simply adjusting the states layer label type-

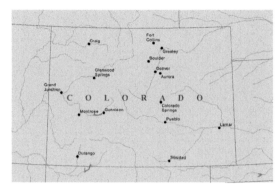

Figure 3.5: Wider populated places labels with word wrap

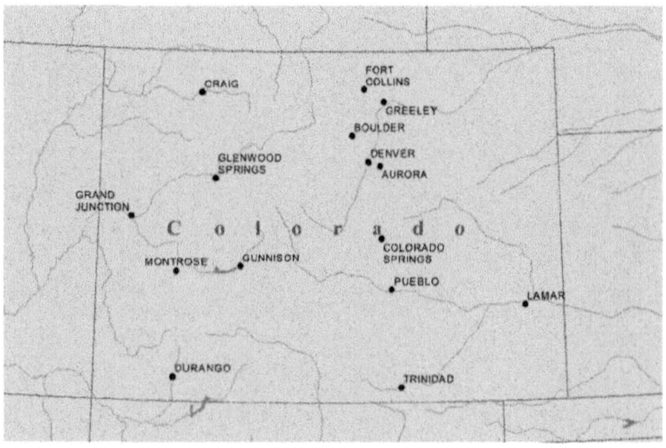

Figure 3.7: The cases are switched here so that the populated places have an even higher visual emphasis over the state label

case to No change as shown in Figure 3.6. This setting causes the labels to appear exactly as they appear in the data, which in this dataset is mixed case.

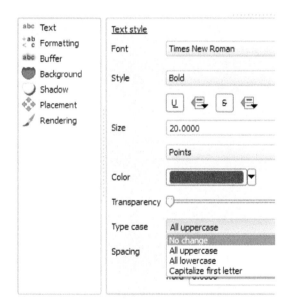

Figure 3.6: Setting the case style for labels

Do the opposite for the populated places layer by changing the typecase to All uppercase. The finished map is shown in Figure 3.7.

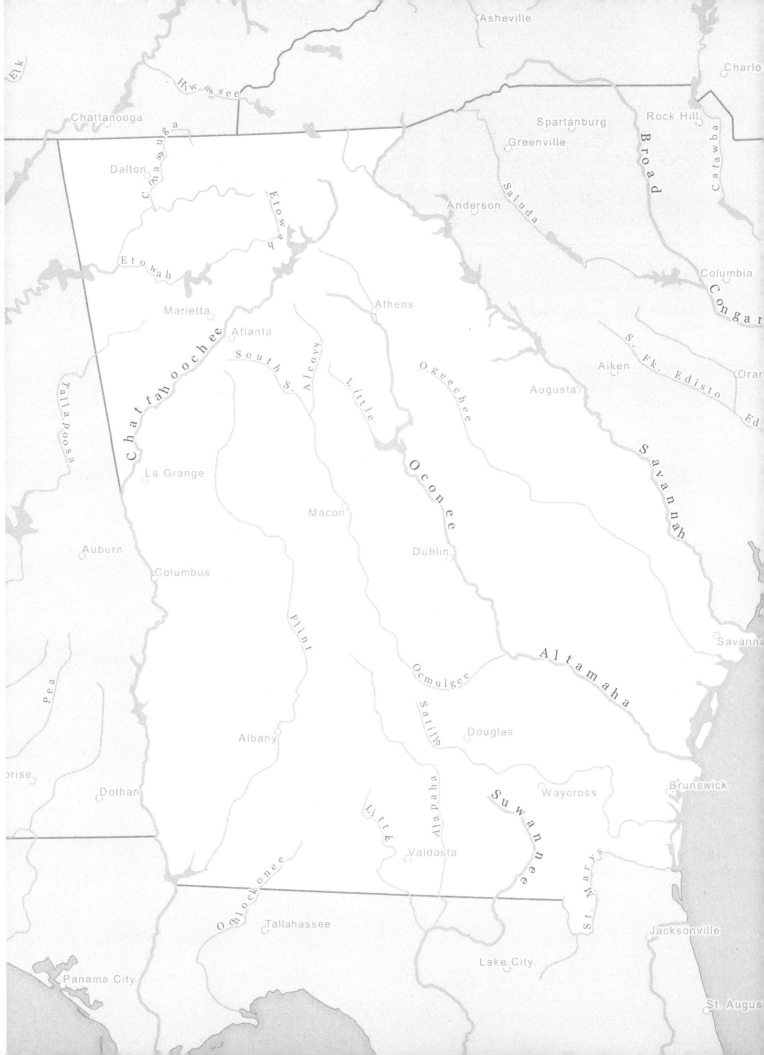

In this recipe, we'll design a map of the rivers of Georgia. The key to creating maps like this is to configure the river labels so they follow the curvy river line geometries.

> To reproduce this map in QGIS, open the river_labels.qgs project.

4.1 Labeling Rivers

Besides the rivers, this map also features oceans, lakes, towns, and of course state borders. We use the following datasets from Natural Earth which you can find in the book resources:

```
ne_10m_populated_places
ne_10m_ocean
ne_10m_lakes
ne_10m_lakes_north_america
ne_10m_rivers_north_america
ne_10m_rivers_lake_centerlines
ne_10_amdin_1_states_provinces
```

First, we'll set up the basic label properties which we would more or less configure for any layer we want to label.

As the names ne_10m_rivers_lake_centerlines (from now on simply referred to as *rivers*) and ne_10m_rivers_north_america (from now on *North American rivers*) suggest, the datasets we are using contain river features as well as lake center line features. To label only river features, we can use the expression shown in Figure 4.1 which checks the featurecla attribute and only labels features where the feature class is 'River'.

A good way to distinguish between different types of labels is to use different fonts and colors. On this map, for example, we label rivers and towns. To visually distinguish between river and town labels and to put emphasis on the rivers, we use dark blue labels in **Georgia** font for the rivers (as shown in Figure 4.2) and medium gray smaller labels in **Arial** for the towns.

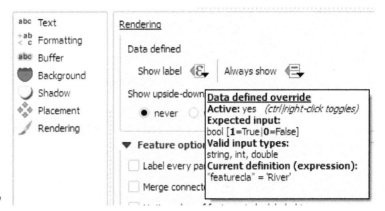

Figure 4.1: Expression to label only river features

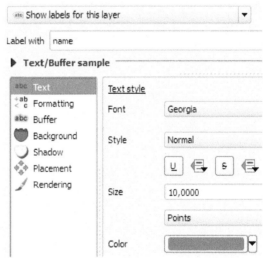

Figure 4.2: Rivers are labeled using Georgia in blue

In addition, all labels on this map use a semi-transparent white **Buffer** as shown in Figure 4.3, on the following page to make them stand out from the map background.

Figure 4.4, on the next page shows the result if we apply these basic settings to the river layer.

While this places some nice straight labels on our river features, clearly, this is not yet what we are looking for. Therefore, with the following steps, we further adjust the settings to cre-

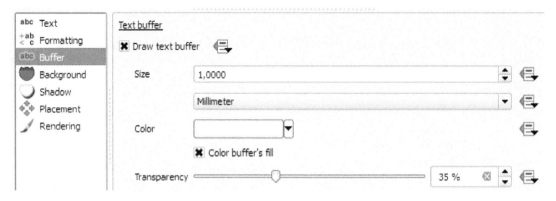

Figure 4.3: Semi-transparent buffers make labels stand out more

Figure 4.4: Labels with basic parallel placement

An alternative approach worth mentioning is to create a generalized line layer which is used for labeling (but not rendering) the rivers. We will explore a similar approach in the Curved Area Labels recipe.

ate labels which are more appropriate for our curvy rivers.

4.2   The Challenge of Curvy Lines

The key to labeling curvy lines is to use Curved label Placement with a Maximum angle between characters tolerance value which is appropriate for your dataset. In our case, we increase the default values from 20 to 50 for both inside and outside angles as shown in Figure 4.5, on the facing page. If you test the curved label placement with the original value of 20, you'll see that only very few, or possibly no rivers at all, are being labeled. This happens because the labeling algorithm cannot find a solution for positioning the label characters in a way that satisfies the placement rules. By increasing the allowed Maximum angle between curved characters, we relax the rules and thus make it possible for the algorithm to place the labels.

Figure 4.6, on the next page shows the resulting labels which follow the curves of the river lines. One downside of increasing the allowed angle between characters is that, in some places, characters are now drawn on top of each other which makes the labels harder or impossible to read.

To overcome this issue, we can increase the Spacing between letters and words. As shown in Figure 4.7, on the facing page, these settings are located at the bottom of the Text style section.

Figures 4.8, on the next page shows the finished labels for the river layer.

The same process—but with slightly smaller font and smaller spacings—is repeated for the

abc Text
+ab
< c Formatting
abc Buffer
⬤ Background
◡ Shadow
✥ Placement
⟋ Rendering

Placement

○ Parallel   ⦿ Curved   ○ Horizontal

Allowed positions [✖] Above line   [ ] On line   [ ] Below line

[ ] Line orientation dependent position

Distance | 0,0000

Millimeter

Repeat | 200,0000

Millimeter

Maximum angle between curved characters

inside | 50,0 | outside | 50,0

Figure 4.5: With curved placement, labels will follow the river shape

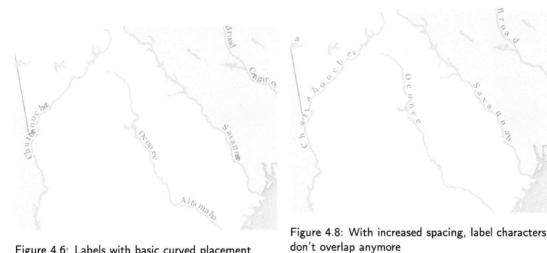

Figure 4.6: Labels with basic curved placement

abc Text
+ab
< c Formatting
abc Buffer
⬤ Background
◡ Shadow
✥ Placement
⟋ Rendering

Text style

Type case | No change

Spacing   letter | 5,0000

word | 6,0000

Blend mode | Normal

Figure 4.7: Increase the spacing to avoid overlapping characters

Figure 4.8: With increased spacing, label characters don't overlap anymore

North American river layer.

4.3   Finishing touches

Once we are happy with the river labels, we can add and label the towns layer. Since these labels are there only to provide some added context, they should visually stay in the background. Therefore, we color the labels gray and use a smaller font (Arial 8.25 pt) with a letter spacing of 1.

The final step to finish the map is to adjust which labels should have higher priority than others. For this map, our main priority is on the rivers. Therefore, we reduce the label Priority of smaller rivers and towns in the Placement section, as shown in Figure 4.9, on the facing page.

Figure 4.10, on the next page shows the final map with its river and town labels.

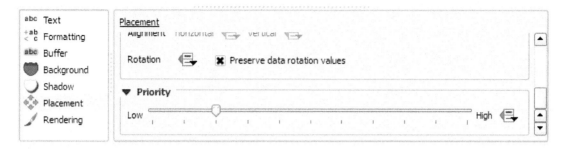

Figure 4.9: Reduce the priority of less important town labels

Figure 4.10: Final labeled river map

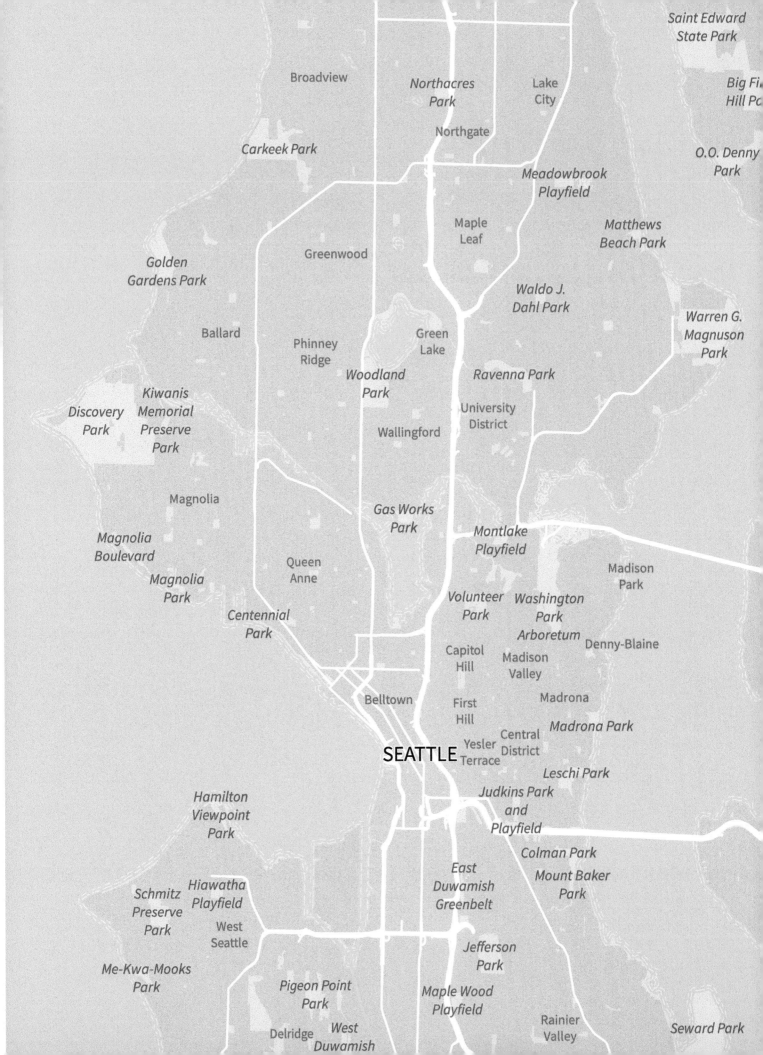

5. Controlling Labels Using Rules, Priority and Features Size Limits

In this recipe, we create a map of the parks in the Seattle region with labels of cities, parks, and city districts. To control which labels get placed if there is not enough space for all of them, we'll configure different label priorities. In addition, we won't label very small parks to avoid cluttering the map.

As an extra, this recipe demonstrates how to create a "*stitched shoreline*" effect for your water areas.

> To reproduce this map in QGIS, open the `citylabels.qgs` project.

5.1 Setting Up the Map

In this recipe, we'll work with data from the Spatialite file `seattle_osm.db`, database, using the points (for city and district labels), lines (roads and rivers), and multipolygons (water, forests & parks, and coastline features) tables.

Figure 5.1 shows the rule-based renderer for the multipolygons layer which defines styles for water areas, forests and parks, as well as coastline features. While the forest, park, and coastline feature symbols are simple polygon fills, the water style uses a stitched shoreline effect.

To create this "stitched shoreline" look, we add two **Simple line** symbol layers to the water symbol as shown in Figure 5.2. One of the lines has an **Offset** of **0.6** Millimeters and the other of **1.4** Millimeters. This offset moves the lines inside the polygon symbol rather than drawing them along the actual polygon outline.

One of the key settings necessary for this effect is that we use different custom dash patterns for the the two lines. Figure 5.3 shows the dash pattern settings used in this recipe. Note that we use a mix of different values for dash and space length. When designing your own effect, make sure to avoid equally spaced dashes.

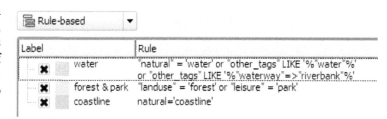

Figure 5.1: The polygon layer is styled with three rules

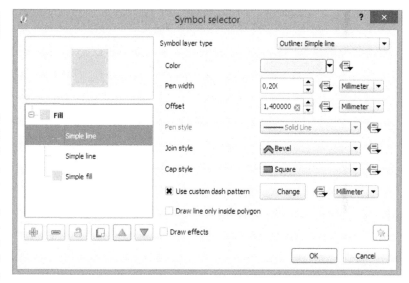

Figure 5.2: Add two outline symbol layers to create the stitched shoreline effect

The colors used in the background map are #e9cda6 for the land areas, #b5cae1 for the water, and #cbdfaa for the parks.

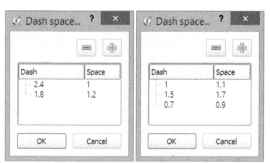

Figure 5.3: Use different custom dash patterns for the outline symbol layers

Besides the polygon layer, this map also features linear features. For this map, we only show roads and rivers from the line layer. The roads are limited to motorways and primary roads and are drawn in white while the rivers are drawn using the same blue we used for the water areas. Figure 5.4 shows the resulting base map.

Figure 5.4: Base map with stitched shoreline effect

5.2   Label Rules for Different Types of Places

For this map, we want to distinguish between labels for important places such as cities and towns and less important place labels such as town districts. To this end, we use rule-based labeling with the two rules shown in Figure 5.5.

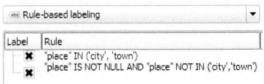

Figure 5.5: Use different label rules for different place types

The city/town labels are black and with a text size of **16 pt** and white buffers. The other place labels are brown (**#956f54**) in size **10 pt** and light brown buffers (**#e9cda6**). We put additional emphasis on city/town labels by setting the **Type case** to **All uppercase**.

To make sure that the Seattle city label is placed directly on top of the corresponding point, we change the label **Placement**, to **Offset from point** over the central **Quadrant**. For the other rule, we leave the default setting **Cartographic**. This option determines cartographically ideal placements, which result in the best visual relationship with the point feature.

Since the place names can be quite long, we wrap the names to avoid wide labels. The following expression wraps the label text to the ideal maximum length of 8 characters:

```
wordwrap(name,8)
```

To make the resulting multiline labels more visually appealing, we set the **Alignment** to **Center**.

Finally, to ensure that the labeling algorithm treats the labels for cities and towns with higher priority, we increase the **PlacementPriority** to the highest possible setting (which equals **10**) as shown in Figure 5.6, on the next page while we leave the district label priority at the default level (**5**).

Figure 5.6: Increase the priority of the city and town label rule

Figure 5.7 shows the resulting map.

Figure 5.7: Seattle is labeled in uppercase while the other labels are less prominent

5.3 Labeling Parks

Since we only want to label park polygons, we use the Data defined Show label expression:

```
"leisure" = 'park'
```

To distinguish parks from district labels, we set the font to **11pt** Italic and use a green color (**#528447**). Since we are more interested in parks than in districts in this recipe, we increase the park label priority to above average (for example, to **8**).

Instead of simply placing the label on top or around the polygon centroid, we enable Horizontal label Placement. This option lets the labeling algorithm find the best horizontal label position for each park label. The resulting map is shown in Figure 5.8.

Figure 5.8: When all parks are labeled, the map is rather crowded

Some of the parks are so small that we don't want them to be labeled. We can define a minimum feature size which is required for labeling by setting the **Suppress labeling of features smaller than** option in the **Rendering** section to, for example, `3.00 mm`, as shown in Figure 5.9.

Figure 5.9: Reduce clutter by only labeling bigger parks

As a result, only big parks are labeled, as shown in Figure 5.10.

Figure 5.10: Fewer park labels make for a much cleaner look

Furthermore, we can reduce the number of labels which cover road features by enabling **Discourage other labels from covering features in this layer** in the line layer's **Labels** settings. Figure 5.11 shows the final map.

Figure 5.11: Final map of parks in the Seattle region

Asahi-dake
(2290)

Iwate-san
(2038)

Tate-yama
(3015)

Fuji
(3776)

Ishizuchi-san
(1982)

Kuju-san
(1788)

Unzen-dake
(1500)

Sakurajima
(1117)

Yonaha-dake
(498)

6. Multi-Attribute Labels and Spatial Filters

In this recipe, we'll create a map of the mountains of Japan which provides the reader information on the mountain names and elevation. To display the information, we'll use multiline labels.

As an extra, this recipe demonstrates how to use a spatial filter to render only features within a certain area—only mountains in Japan.

> To reproduce this map in QGIS, open the multiline_labels_japan.qgs project.

6.1 Preparing the Base Map

For this map, we use two datasets from Natural Earth:

```
ne_10m_geography_regions_elevation_points
ne_10m_admin_0_countries
```

To highlight Japan on the map, a rule-based renderer is used which checks for the feature name value and draws Japan in orange. On top of this background, we place the global elevation points layer.

6.2 Applying a Spatial Filter

To only show mountains in Japan on our map, we create the following spatial filter rule:

```
intersects($geometry,
  geom_from_wkt('Polygon((126.76 31.68,
  142.27 44.77, 148.18 42.30, 140.02 32.57,
  131.47 26.35, 126.24 25.44, 126.76 31.68))
  '))
```

This rule checks if the elevation point is located within the yellow area depicted in Figure 6.1, which contains all Japanese mountains.

Figure 6.1: The spatial filter polygon contains all Japanese mountain features

6.3 Scaling Mountain Symbols

For the mountain symbol, we use a triangle with data-defined size depending on the elevation value as shown in Figure 6.2, on the following page:

```
"elevation" / 200.0
```

This results in bigger triangles for higher mountains. Figure 6.3, on the next page shows the final styling for the elevation points layer.

121

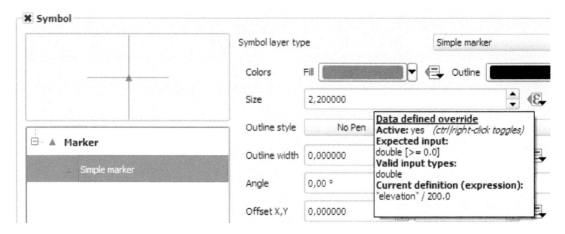

Figure 6.2: Use a triangle to symbolize the mountains

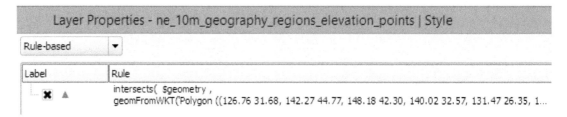

Figure 6.3: Rule with spatial filter for Japanese mountains

6.4 Creating Multi-Attribute Labels

For the labels on this map, we use the open source font *Source Sans Pro* (which you can find in the book resources), along with a semi-transparent white buffer.

On the map, we want to display both the name and the elevation of the mountains. To do that, we need to *concatenate* the name and elevation fields. The full expression is:

```
name || '\n(' || elevation || ')'
```

and consists of the following parts: || is the concatenation operator which can be used to chain strings together. The '\n(' inserts a line break and opens the brackets around the elevation value. Finally, we close the brackets again. Figure 6.4, on the facing page shows this expression in the Label with field.

Figure 6.4, on the next page shows how to fine-tune the distance between mountain symbol and label. Since our symbols scale with the

elevation values, a fixed distance would result in different gaps between symbols and labels. We can avoid this effect by making the distance data-defined as well. For this map, we'll use the distance expression:

```
sqrt(elevation/1000)
```

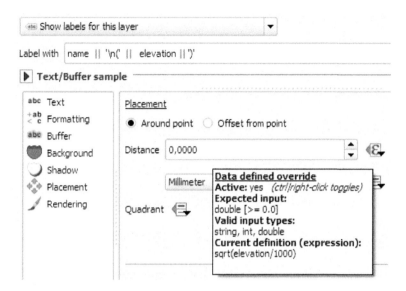

Figure 6.4: Data-defined distance between symbol and label

6.5 Finishing Touches

The left side of Figure 6.5 shows the labels generated using these settings.

Figure 6.5: Multiline labels with default alignment

Not bad, but note how all our multiline labels are aligned to the left, even if it would be more appropriate to have different alignments corresponding to the respective label's position as shown on the right side of Figure 6.6.

To achieve this effect, we change the **Alignment** setting in the **Formatting** section from **Left** to **Follow label placement** as shown in Figure 6.7.

Figure 6.6: Multiline labels with and adaptive alignment

Figure 6.7: Change the alignment to make it adapt to the label placement

7. Placing Labels by Hand for Small Area Features

This recipe illustrates how to use the label toolbar to manually place labels on a map. This recipe becomes the basis for the Overview Maps recipe, on page 169 in the Print Map Design section, on page 140.

> To reproduce this map in QGIS, open the handplaced_labels.qgs project.

There are several ways to position labels in QGIS: making use of the label toolbar, creating a new point layer, or using the add label tool in the print composer. In this recipe, we'll focus on the first method, using the label toolbar. Many of the tools are grayed out initially because there are a few set-up steps are required before they can be used. First, we'll add some layers to the project and style them, then we'll label one of the layers using the label toolbar.

7.1 Styling the Base Layers

Add the following raster and vector datasets to the project:

```
NE1_LR_LC
ne_10m_ocean
ne_10m_lakes
ne_10m_parks_and_protected_lands_area
```

Change the CRS to 102008 (North America Albers Equal Area Conic), and zoom to the U.S. Southwest location shown on the final map at the beginning of this recipe.

Change the color of the ocean layer to the preset color called water. Copy the ocean style and paste it to the lakes layer. Create a 50% transparency on the parks layer and also fill them with #33a02c (green) and use a border color of #33672c (a slightly darker green). Parks are often symbolized with a green fill and a darker green outline and we'll stick with that convention here.

The labels we're interested in showing on the map are the park names. Use the Layer Properties, Labels dialog to take a look at how the labels will look in their default locations. Use the name field for labeling and Times New Roman for the font.

Traditionally, serif fonts like this are used for labeling natural features. National Parks are human constructs but they essentially demarcate natural features, so a serif font appears consistent with accepted cartographic practice. Use a size 8 pt font in the same green hue as the national park borders and enable word wrapping by setting the wrap to a space (as in the Typecase recipe, on page 105). The line height is set to 0.8 and the alignment is set to center. Also make sure to use a 0.5 millimeter text buffer set to a dominant background color (we used #eddac7).

Hint: Use the color picker tab found in the Color selector dialog. Select a large Sample average radius and click Sample color to make it easy to pick a suitable color from the map.

At this stage the map will appear as shown in Figures 7.1 and 7.2, on the next page.

Figure 7.1: The national park map with labels placed automatically

Figure 7.2: A closer look at the default map labels

7.2 Hand Placing Labels

Since the park areas are small, long, and narrow, the labels appear to cover up much of the area they are labeling. We'll use the label toolbar to move them to better locations.

In order to use the label toolbar, a dataset must have fields named x, y, and rotation. Add the required fields to the attribute table for the parks layer by enabling editing mode and adding columns with those names and the properties as shown in Figure 7.3. (Make sure to set a useful width and precision and keep the Type as Decimal.)

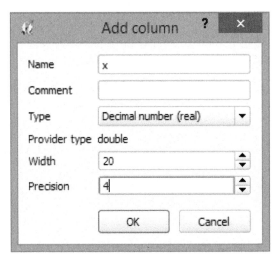

Figure 7.3: Adding the x column for label placement

Note that the parks layer in the geodata folder with the "labels1" suffix already has these columns in it. To get the most out of this exercise use the parks layer that doesn't have that suffix so that you can add the columns yourself.

Now that the dataset contains the columns where the label placement geometry will be written to by QGIS, we'll tell QGIS to use them. In the data defined placement section of the la-

bel placement menu, click the double-rectangle button (override button) found next to X, point to field type, and choose the x column that was just created. This process is shown in Figure 7.4, on the next page.

Repeat this process for the Y and Rotation overrides except using the columns y and rotation, respectively. The override buttons turn yellow in edit mode when they are activated in this way.

Make sure your label toolbar is active via the View, Toolbars, Label Toolbar option in the main menu, and also that the parks layer is in editing mode. You should see that the label tools are activated (i.e., not grayed out) at this stage, as shown in Figure 7.5, on the facing page.

Now the *move label*, *rotate label*, and *change label* buttons in the label toolbar will be available to use.

By clicking on the move label tool and then clicking on one of the labels, you can move the label by dragging it. If you are creating a Print Composer layout for the map, getting the optimal placement may take some trial and error. In the parks labels layer (geodata folder, ne_10m_parks_and_protected_lands_area_labels) we've placed the labels optimally for the layout that we'll create in the Overview Maps recipe in the next section of the book. We also deleted a few of the park labels we didn't want to appear in the layout for that recipe. See the finished map at the beginning of this recipe.

Figure 7.4: Using the new columns as override label placement columns

Figure 7.5: The label toolbar

In this recipe, we will continue the work on our Google Maps inspired map (Styling OSM Roads Like Google Maps, on page 73) by adding road and building labels.

> To reproduce this map in QGIS, open the `google_road_labels.qgs` project.

8.1 Labels for Roads

To label only road lines, we use the data-defined Show label expression:

```
"highway" is not null
```

The key to labeling roads is to make sure that **Merge connected lines to avoid duplicate labels** is enabled in the **Rendering** section. This makes sure that the labeling algorithm does not place the same label again and again for each line feature of the same named road. In case of longer roads, it can be nice to repeat the label after a certain distance. This can be achieved by setting the **Repeat** value in the **Placement** section to, for example, 120 millimeters.

To reproduce the Google Maps style, we also need to activate **Curved Placement** with **On line** position as shown in Figure 8.1.

To make sure that more important roads are labeled first, we can define the data-defined **Priority** in the **Placement** section as shown in Figure 8.2. This expression returns the highest priority value **10** for motorways and decreasingly smaller values for less important road classes.

The final step to recreate the labeling shown in Figure 8.3, on the following page is to configure the buffer color to reflect the road color. This effect can be created using the following expression for the data-defined buffer color:

```
CASE
 WHEN "highway" = 'motorway'
  THEN color_rgb(250,158,37)
 WHEN "highway" IN ('motorway_link','trunk',
```

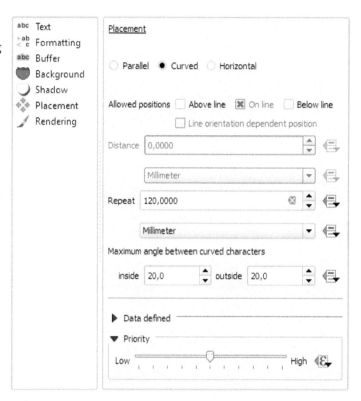

Figure 8.1: Place road labels on the line and make them repeat

Figure 8.2: Label priority depends on road class

129

```
                      'primary','primary_link')
    THEN color_rgb(255,225,104)
    ELSE color_rgb(255,255,255)
END
```

Figure 8.3: Basic road labels with differently colored buffers

Figure 8.4: Shorten road names and combine them with the road reference code

We used the same classification to style the roads.

It is worth noting, that we could have used rule-based labeling to create different rules with different labeling settings. We decided against rule-based labeling in this recipe since the road labels are very similar with only minor differences such as buffer color and placement priority. Therefore, it is easier to configure and maintain the labels in one place instead of having to update multiple rules to change, for example, the label font.

8.2 Fine-tuning and Road Reference Codes

We could be perfectly happy with our label configuration now, but if you have a look around the map you'll notice that quite a few motorways are not labeled at all. Why is that? Simply because their `name` field is `NULL`. Instead, you will find that there is a road reference code such as:

```
"ref"=>"I 5 Express"
```

hidden in the `other_tags` field. Figure 8.4 shows the Label with expression magic we can use to extract this road reference code (and also shorten the labels a little while we're at it).

Consult the help section in the Expression string builder to learn more about which functions you can use in your expressions.

While this might look kind of intimidating, we can take it apart and see what the different parts of this expression accomplish. On the first line, we see the `concat` function. This just

makes sure everything we pass into it is concatenated into one long string. The second line uses the `replace` function to shorten `'Avenue'` and `'Boulevard'` to `'Av.'` and `'Bd.'`, respectively. The `CASE` statement that follows checks if the `other_tags` field contains `extquotedblref extquotedbl=> extquotedbl`. If this is the case, the combination of `left` and `right` function extracts the road reference code from the `other_tags` field.

8.3 Labels for Buildings

To add more context to our map, it's nice to also label the buildings. The buildings are part of the polygon layer. In order to label only building polygons, we use the following data-defined Show label expression:

```
"building" is not null
```

To fit the building name labels inside the building polygons, we first of all use a narrow font such as Yanone Kaffeesatz (you can locate and install this font from the resources folder), but that's not enough. We also need to split long labels into multiple lines. This can be achieved using the Label with expression:

```
wordwrap("name",12)
```

which wraps the name string to a maximum of 12 characters. For example, the building named `City Centre Building` gets a line break inserted between `Centre` and `Building`.

Don't forget to set the **Alignment** to **Center** in the **Formatting** section otherwise, the multiline labels will be left aligned.

Another key to reproducing these building labels is to set the **Placement** to **Free**. This allows the labeling algorithm to compute the optimal rotation angle for the labels as shown in Figure 8.5.

Figure 8.5: Map with building labels

8.4   Finishing Touches

Finally, we add city and district labels. Of course this is optional but it provides another layer of context for the map readers.

To place these labels at the exact point positions, we use the **Placement** option **Offset from point** combined with the central **Quadrant** as shown in Figure 8.6.

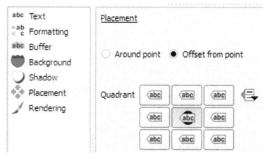

Figure 8.6: Put the place labels directly on top of the points

Finally, we vary the font size based on the place type using the following expression:

```
CASE WHEN "place" IN ('city', 'town')
     THEN 12
     ELSE 8
END
```

In this recipe, we'll create a map of the seas surrounding the Philippines. What makes this map special is, we'll not be content with the basic polygon labels which the labeling algorithms can create automatically. Instead, we will create our own custom layer for label placement.

To reproduce this map in QGIS, open the curved_area_labels.qgs project.

9.1 Setting Up the Map

We'll use the following datasets from Natural Earth which you can find in the book resources:

```
ne_10m_populated_places
ne_10m_admin_0_countries
```

Since we want to create white land features, we change the map **Background color** in the **Project Properties General** section to a darker color, for example **#9fd9c9** as shown in Figure 9.1.

If we style the country layer in white and zoom to the Philippines, the resulting map looks like Figure 9.2.

For more geographic context, add the populated places layer which we can style based on the **FEATURECLA** attribute as shown in Figure 9.3.

The labels are quite basic black with white semi-transparent buffers. We reduce the label **Size** from **10** to **8** for points with the **FEATURECLA** value 'Populated place' using the expression:

```
CASE WHEN "FEATURECLA" = 'Populated place'
THEN 8 ELSE 10 END
```

Figure 9.4, on the next page shows the resulting map

Now that the basic map is set up, we can advance to creating the labels for the seas surrounding the Philippines.

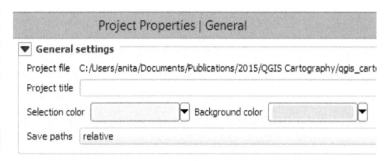

Figure 9.1: Change the background color to make it possible to see white land polygons

Figure 9.2: The Philippines in white stand out on top of the colorful background

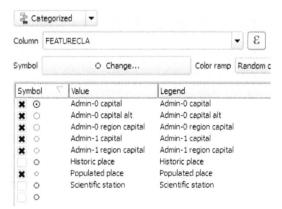

Figure 9.3: Use different symbols for different place types

Figure 9.4: Place labels add additional detail to our map

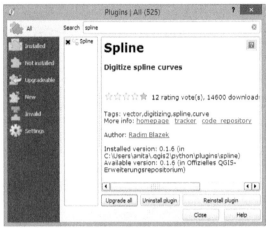

Figure 9.5: Install the Splines plugin

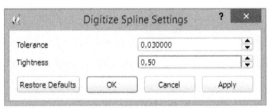

Figure 9.6: Configure the Spline tool

9.2 Creating Curved Area Labels

If you want to skip the layer creation and go straight to the labeling part, you can add the ne_10m_geography_marine_polys_labels dataset.

You can access the Plugin Manager from the Plugins menu, Manage and Install Plugins

The idea is to create a dedicated layer where we draw the lines that the labels should follow. A very useful tool for drawing these curved label lines is the Spline plugin. You can install this plugin using the Plugin Manager: As shown in Figure 9.5, you can use the **Search** bar at the top of the Plugin Manager dialog to look for the Spline plugin. Then select it from the list and press the **Install** plugin button.

Once you have installed the plugin, you'll find it in the **Vector** menu. Before we start drawing the lines, adjust the Spline plugin settings as shown in Figure 9.6.

We also need to create a line layer to hold the features. For this example, create a new Shapefile using **Layer | Create Layer | New Shapefile Layer ....** In the **New Vector Layer** dialog, we can specify the attributes we need, that is, a string attribute to hold the label text as well as an integer attribute to hold the label size. Figure 9.7 shows the settings.

Now we can start drawing our label curves us-

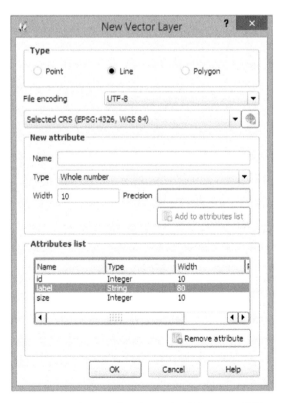

Figure 9.7: The new line layer should contain fields to hold label text and size

ing the Digitize Spline Curves tool which you should find in the plugin toolbar as shown in Figure 9.8. If you cannot find it, you can enable the toolbar using the View, Toolbars menu.

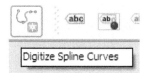

Figure 9.8: The Spline tool is added to the plugin toolbar

Click on a location on the map to start drawing a line. When you have placed the second point and are moving toward the third, you'll notice the spline tool starts approximating a curve to fit through the points you clicked. When the line is complete, right click to stop drawing. This brings up the attribute form where we can enter the label text and the desired font size. Figure 9.9 shows the lines we have created in the `ne_10m_geography_marine_polys_labels` dataset.

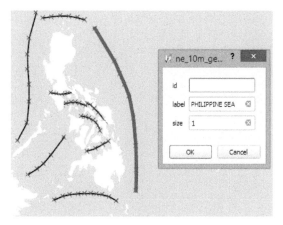

Figure 9.9: Use the Spline tool to create the curved lines for our labels

9.3 Varying Font Sizes

In this recipe, we play with different font sizes to reflect the size/importance of the labeled area. To get the font sizes right usually requires some trial and error. To create font size settings which will work on any zoom level, we configure the label size units to Map unit instead of Points. Figure 9.10 shows the label settings where both the font size and the letter spacing depend on the `size` attribute value.

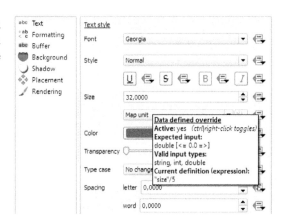

Figure 9.10: The label size and letter spacing depend on the size attribute value

A convenient way to fine-tune the label size values is to use the Change label tool from the labeling toolbar. This tool becomes available when we configure a label size field and the layer is in editing mode. Figure 9.11 shows the Label properties dialog that appears when we use the Change label tool to click on a label.

Figure 9.11: Customizing labels is very convenient with the Change label tool

The remaining labeling settings are quite basic with a buffer color of `#67c3aa` and Curved On line Placement. Figure 9.12, on the next page shows the configured curved area labels.

Make sure to set the Placement Priority to above average to ensure that our sea area labels have higher priority than the labels of the populated places layer as shown in Figure 9.13, on the following page.

Once you are happy with the curved labels, you

can make the line symbol completely transparent to hide the fact that we are using a line layer to place our labels.

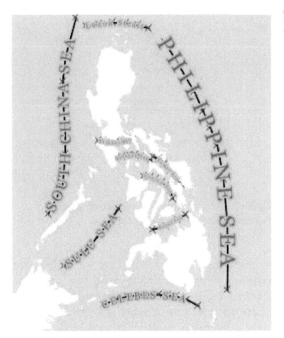

Figure 9.12: Getting the font sizes right usually requires some manuall back and forth tweaking

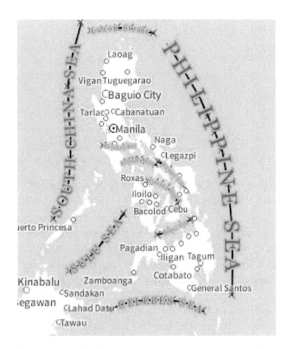

Figure 9.13: Make sure to increase the priority of our curved area labels

9.4 Bonus: Background Texture

To make this map even more special, we can add a background texture to fill the water areas of the map background. In this recipe, we use a texture from the online collection at lostandtaken.com[20].

As you can see in Figure 9.14, on the next page, we go to the print composer to add the background texture. The key is to add a picture item behind the map item. In the picture's Item properties panel, we can pick the Image source file watercolor14.jpg.

Working with the print composer is covered in detail in the Designing print maps recipes in the last part of this book, on page 140.

The textures of lostandtaken.com are free to use for any purpose.

20. http://loc8.cc/qmd/watercolor

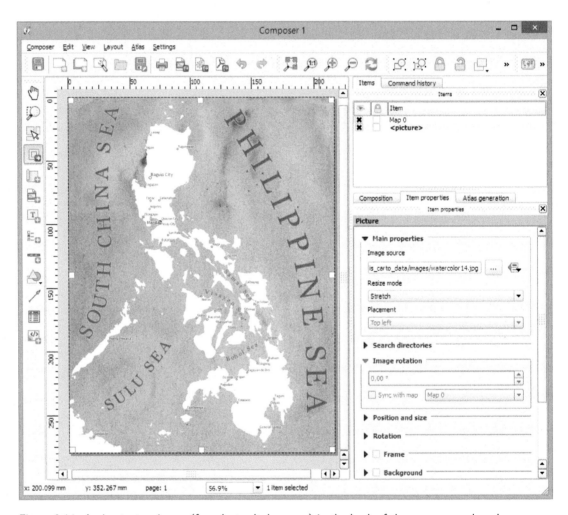

Figure 9.14: A nice texture image (from lostandtaken.com) in the back of the map can make a huge difference

Part 3

Print Map Design

COFFEE IN SEATTLE

people in Seattle consume more coffee than in any other American city

One study stated that there are 35 coffeeshops per 100,000 residents and that Seattle people spend an average of $36 a month on coffee.

It is nearly impossible to walk past a single block in a commercial area in Seattle without walking past at least one coffee shop.

Coffee drinkers can get coffee at a local sidewalk stand, parking lot, tiny coffee houses, big coffee houses, drive-through, and even delivery. *wikipedia*

1. Learning Layout Basics with the Seattle Coffee Map

This recipe explores the QGIS layout tools by creating a U.S. letter-sized print composer layout, building on the map from the Text Buffers recipe, on page 101. We'll use that map at a smaller scale and add some basic margin information to illustrate the print capabilities in QGIS.

> To reproduce this map in QGIS, open the layout_basics.qgs project or begin with the finished map from text_buffers.qgs and build up from there.

1.1 Tweaking for Scale

There are times when you'll have to tweak map styles to accommodate a different scale. In the text_buffers project we were working on a larger scale than we are in this map. If you're beginning with the recipe from the Text Buffers project, change the scale to about 1:15,000 and pan the map to approximately the location of the final map shown at the beginning of this recipe.

The coffee shop icons need to be smaller—change them to 4 millimeters. At this point, notice that the coffee mug icons appear to be too thick. Adjust their outline size downward to 0.2 millimeters. The labels also need to be smaller—adjust them so that they are 8 pt with a buffer size of 0.8, and change the placement to 1.4 mm around the points. Leave all the other label information the same.

1.2 Creating a Layout in QGIS

With those tweaks made to the map, we can now create the layout. In QGIS, you can export a map straight from the main window using the Project, Save as image... menu, which is helpful for quick exports but doesn't provide any ability to include legends, north arrows, scale bars, titles or any other finishing map items to the display. Layouts are created in the QGIS Print Composer window. You can make one or more print composers in a project.

The Print Composer allows you to set the exported page size, add the map you just created to it (and any other maps you end up creating), and margin information such as the legend and title. It also provides the capability to align and distribute these items to create a nice looking layout. It provides much more as well, which we will delve into in other recipes.

To begin, go to Project, New Print Composer. Give it the name BasicLayout at the prompt (if you're working with the finished project file, there is already a print composer called BasicLayout that contains the finished layout for this recipe, so in this case you would need to provide a different name).

The default page size is set to the European standard A4. Change this to U.S. letter, or ANSI A, in the composition tab at the right-hand side of the page under Page size.

The Composition tab and the Item properties tab are used frequently during the design of a map layout. The composition tab provides an interface to input general specifications for the entire layout while the item properties tab contains the ability to change properties for specific elements on a layout such as the font size for a text box, the rotation for a map, or the items in a legend.

Activate snapping so that all the items that are added to the layout can stay in alignment with the page by clicking View, Snap to Grid. You can also click Show Grid in the same menu if want the grid visible while you work.

This map layout will have a dark brown frame that could be created a few different ways. In this exercise a simple rectangle will suffice. To create the rectangle, use the Add Shape, Add Rectangle tool from the left-hand side of the print composer window. With that tool activated you can now click and drag a rectangle across the page. Adjust it so it is snapped to the edges of the layout. To change it to the dark brown color, use the Item properties tab, which, because the rectangle is active, contains all the rectangle-specific properties that can be adjusted. Under Shape, Main properties you'll notice there is a color changer where the color should be changed to #34181c.

Along the left-hand side of the print composer you'll also see the Add new map tool. Use this to drag an area for the map to go, so that it is within the rectangle that's already there as shown in Figure 1.1, on the facing page.

If the Items window isn't open, open it in View menu, Panels, Items.

Notice that the Items tab in the upper-right portion of the print composer window has two items listed: Map 0 and <rectangle> that correspond to the map that was just placed and the background rectangle. The items list is useful for quickly selecting an item on the layout, especially when there are many items. Of course, the items can also be selected with the mouse, visually, on the layout preview itself.

One trick for getting the extent the way you'd like it is to change the size of the main QGIS window so that the map canvas is the actual size of the map that you'd like to export or print.

At this point it's important to modify the extent of the map. There are a few ways to do this but in this exercise just go back to the main map window and pan and zoom, then go back to the print composer and use the Set to map canvas extent for this modification. Aim for an extent close to what is shown in Figure 1.2, on the next page.

Add a couple of images to the layout using the Add image tool, dragging a rectangle on the layout page, and then setting the path to the image file by setting the Image source property in the Item properties tab for that image as shown in Figure 1.3, on page 144.

The first image to add is the coffeebeans.png image located in the resources folder. Similarly, add the coffeecup.png image to the layout.

To create the background rectangle for the title and text area, we'll use a rectangle with a gradient fill that gradually fades into the map.

The gradual fadeout technique integrates the rectangle into the design rather than setting it apart. Create another new rectangle as before, only this time position it so that it covers roughly one-third of the right-hand side of the layout and modify its properties as shown in Figure 1.4, on page 144. Specifically, the style is set to a gradient fill with two colors: transparent and white. The reference point 2 is set to centroid and all the other values are left as-is.

The title of the layout is "COFFEE IN SEATTLE." Each word is in its own text box because each word is a different size. Each of the five explanatory text parts are also in their own text boxes so that their alignment on the page is easier to control.

To place the word "COFFEE" on the page, use the Add new label tool, drag it across the page, and change its item properties so that the word "QGIS" is replaced with "COFFEE," the font is changed to Yanone Kaffeesatz Bold (you can locate and install this font from the resources folder), size 72 pt, and the rotation is set to 330 degrees. The rotation is purposely set to match the general direction of the Seattle street grid.

Add the other parts of the title by copying and pasting the COFFEE text and changing their respective sizes. You can also add more text as desired. In the example map we used text from a Wikipedia article on Seattle coffee to augment the map and styled it with the Gabriola font as shown in the finished map at the beginning of this recipe.

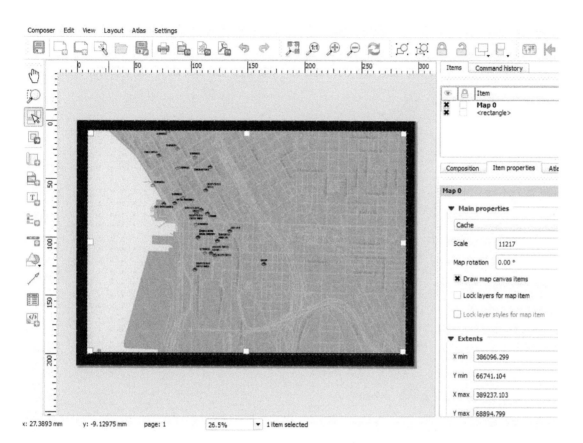

Figure 1.1: Adding the map to the layout

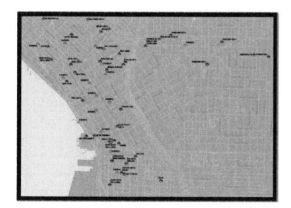

Figure 1.2: Approximate extent for map area

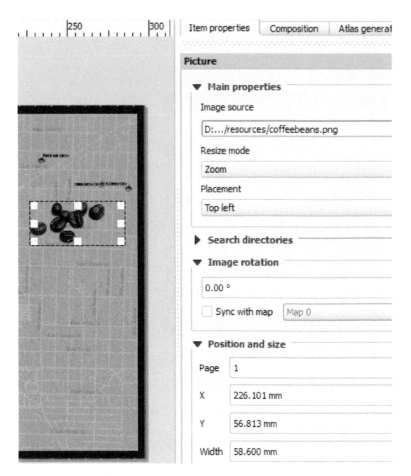

Figure 1.3: Add an image to the layout by specifying the file path

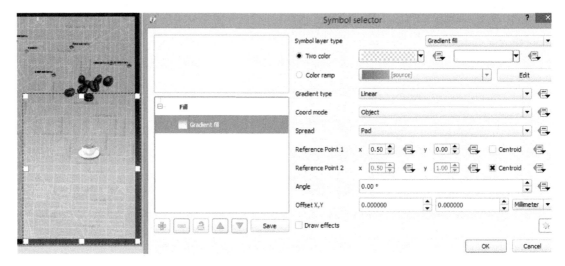

Figure 1.4: Changing rectangle properties to apply a transparency gradient

Most Populous Metropolitan Areas

Most Populous Metropolitan Areas

2. Customizing Legends

In this recipe we'll take the map created in the Restricted Labeling recipe, on page 97 and create a basic print layout for it, containing a title and custom legend. In so doing, we continue to explore the Print Composer, using the extremely handy item customization options found in the Item properties tab.

> To reproduce this map in QGIS, begin with the finished map from the Restricted Labeling recipe, which can be found in the restricted_labeling.qgs project. Alternatively, view this finished recipe in the customized_legend.qgs project.

2.1 Creating a New Print Composer

We'll add one layout (print composer) to this recipe and name it popmap. To do this use the Project, New Print Composer menu as shown in Figure 2.1. Once the Print Composer is open, change the page size to the size that seems appropriate for your use.

Figure 2.1: Providing a title to a new Print Composer window

In the example project you'll notice it's size is set to 8.5" by 5.5," which seems to suit both the aspect ratio of this world level map and the margin elements that will be added to it. U.S. readers will notice that the page size defaults to A4 in new print compositions, which is not the U.S. Standard Letter size.

One of the great things about the QGIS Print Composer is that each item on the layout can be customized in the Item properties tab. The Item properties are shown for the active item in the layout.

2.2 Creating the Layout

To add the map to the page, use the Add new map tool in the left-hand toolbar. It doesn't snap to the page but if you turn on View, Snap to Grid and use the handle boxes to drag the existing map to the corners of the page, you'll notice that it will then snap to the page. This map has enough white space to place the margin items, so it's okay to allow it to take up the entire page.

Adjust the viewing extent by changing the extent of the original map in the main project window so that Antarctica doesn't appear. To view the map at 100%, use Ctrl+1 and then Item properties, Update preview. Or click the Refresh view button on the toolbar. Returning to the Print Composer and clicking the Item properties, Set to map canvas extent button updates the map in the layout to match as shown in Figure 2.2, on the following page.

2.3 Modifying the Default Legend

Add a legend in the lower-left-hand corner using the Add new legend tool in the left-hand toolbar, shown in Figure 2.3, on the next page.

Now the Item properties tab contains the customization options for the legend. First, delete the title text so that Legend no longer appears at the top (in most cases, use of the words *legend*, *key*, or *map key* are superfluous.)

Unchecking the Auto update option in Item properties, Legend allows you to delete legend items, rename them, and change their order. A key isn't necessary for the self-explanatory coun-

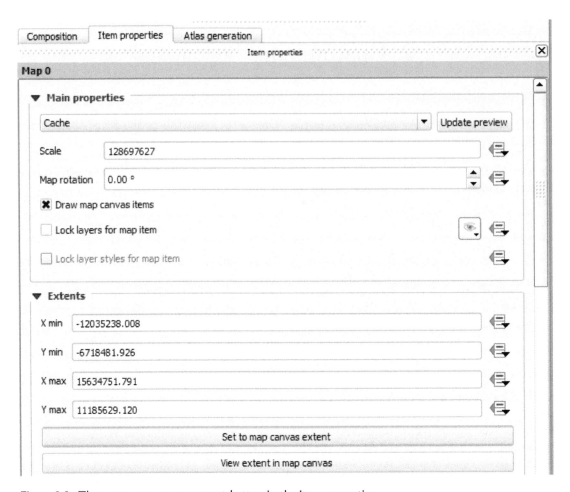

Figure 2.2: The set to map canvas extent button in the item properties

Georgia is a font that has numbers that read like letters due to their varying placement above the baseline. While this can look good inside paragraph text, it doesn't look as good as a single-baseline number system in columns of numbers. The numerals in Arial are all placed directly on the baseline.

Figure 2.3: The Add Legend tool

tries background, so delete the countries layer item from the legend items list.

Because there are no features in the 20 to 30 million category, edit that category with the pencil button so that it reads "20 - 30 (none)" as shown in Figure 2.4, on the facing page. An-

other option would be to gray that portion of the legend a bit to indicate an unused category, but this isn't possible within QGIS at this time.

The subgroup title can also be changed with the pencil button. Here we've shortened it to "Metro Population, Millions" so it doesn't run over South America.

Under Item properties, Legend, fonts, change the subgroup font to Georgia and the item font to Arial. We're using Arial for the items because it tends to look better in columns of text than Georgia. If the frame for the legend is covering up a portion of the map, uncheck the Item properties, Background option. Finally, add a title for the map using the Add new label button in the left-hand toolbar. Once you've used this tool to drag a title box onto the page, you may notice that you can't modify the text by typing directly inside the resulting rectangle.

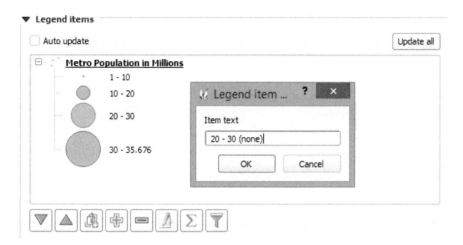

Figure 2.4: Adding custom text to a category

In QGIS, text is added in the Item properties, Main properties box as shown in Figure 2.5, on the next page.

The font and text size is changed in the Appearance section as shown in Figure 2.6, on the following page.

The final map is shown, along with an inverted color scheme, at the beginning of this recipe.

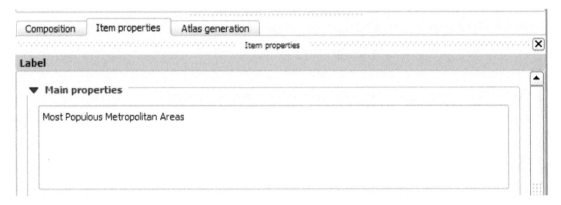

Figure 2.5: The text input box for layout labels

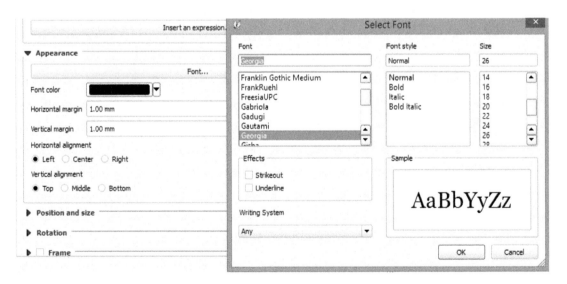

Figure 2.6: Font specifications for layout labels

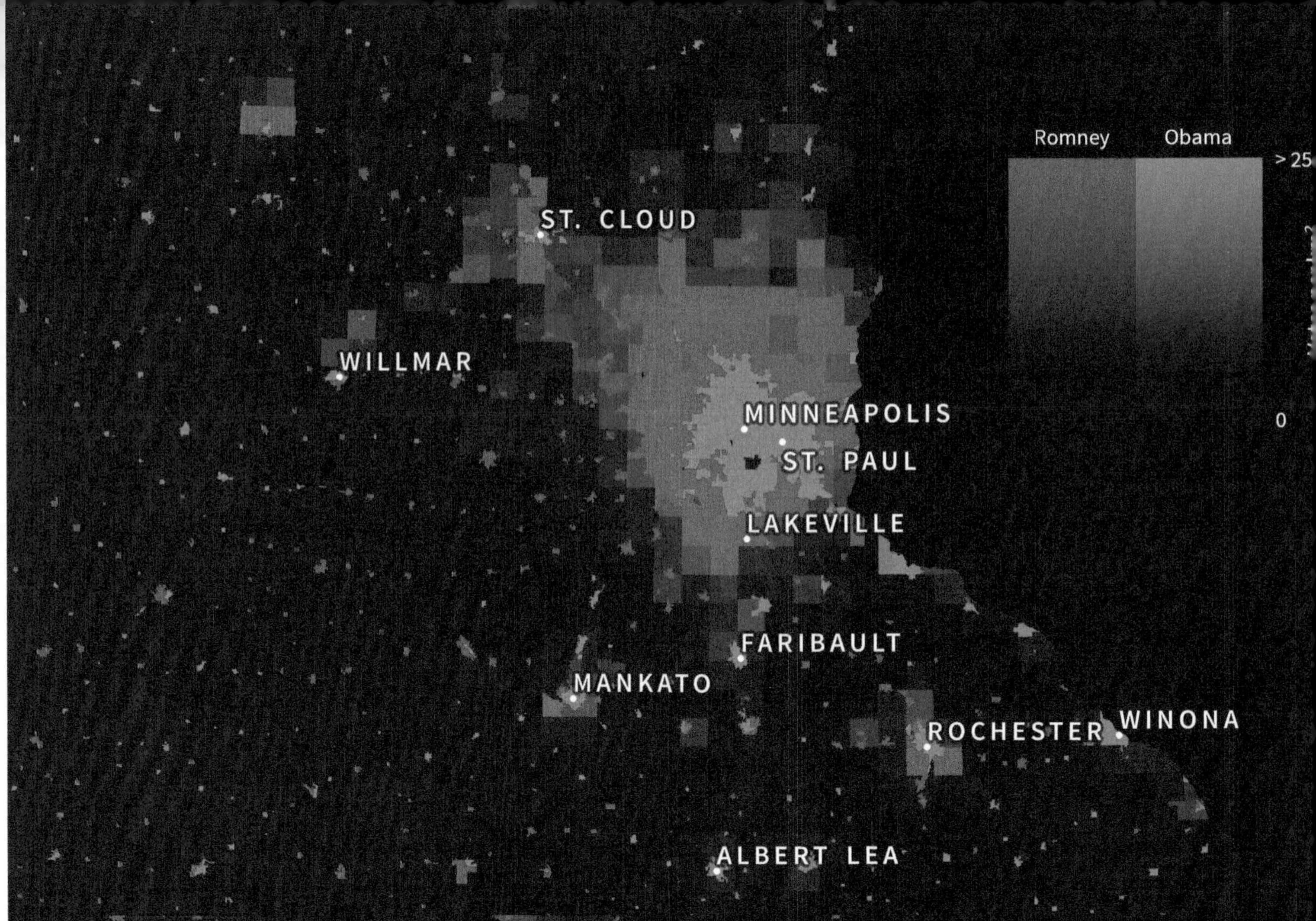
Romney
Obama
> 25
0
ST. CLOUD
WILLMAR
MINNEAPOLIS
ST. PAUL
LAKEVILLE
FARIBAULT
MANKATO
ROCHESTER
WINONA
ALBERT LEA

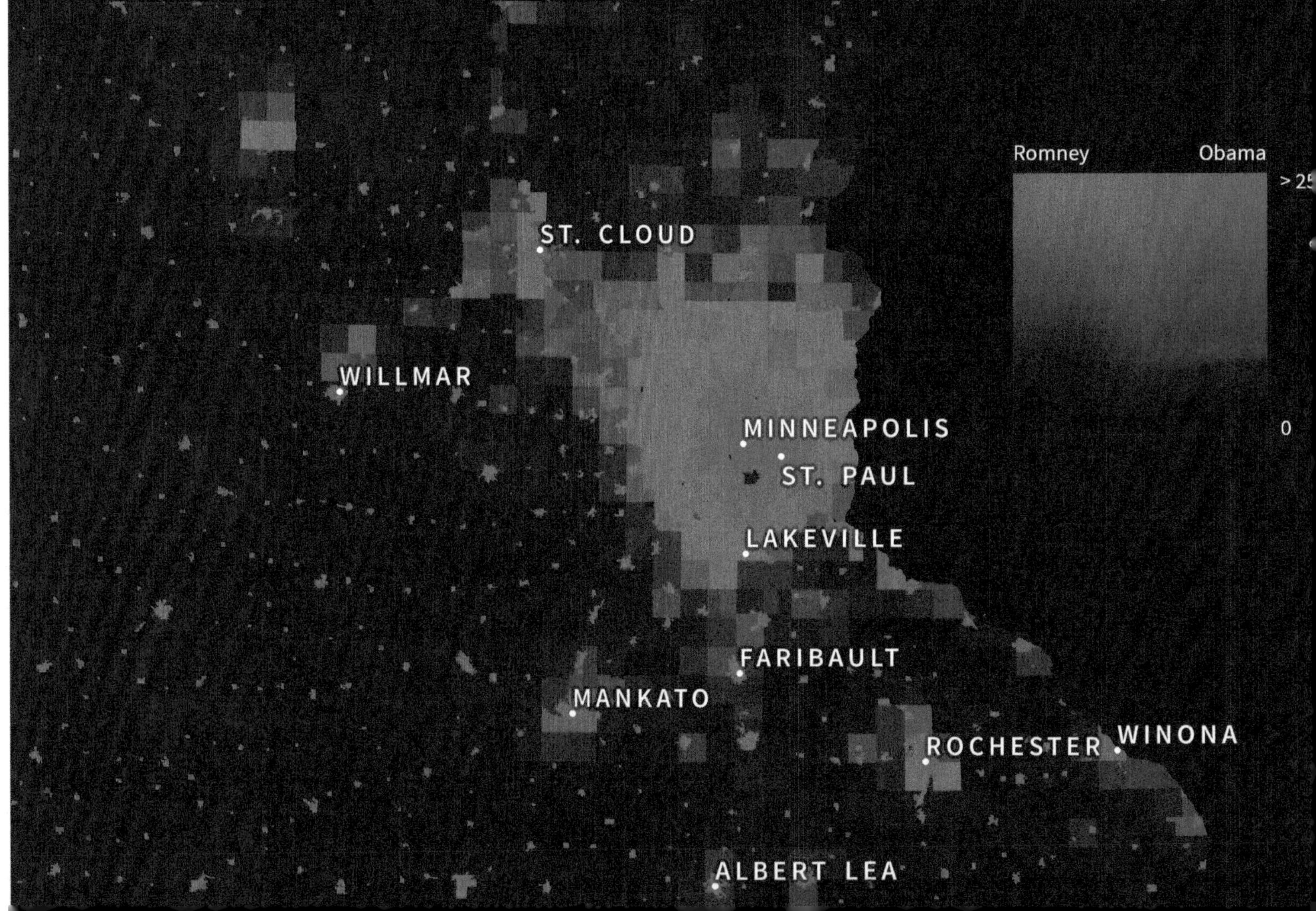
Romney
Obama
> 25
0
ST. CLOUD
WILLMAR
MINNEAPOLIS
ST. PAUL
LAKEVILLE
FARIBAULT
MANKATO
ROCHESTER
WINONA
ALBERT LEA

In this recipe, we'll build custom gradient legends. We'll create two different legend versions which complete our value by alpha voting map recipe (Mapping Election Results by Votes Cast, on page 79). The first legend example combines solid colors with a gradient. The second shows a slight modification of the voting map which abandons the original binary style and uses a smooth gradient to show how the votes were split between candidates.

> To reproduce this map in QGIS, open the `gradient_legend.qgs` project.

3.1 Solid Color and Gradient Legend

This map shows the winning candidate as well as the voter density. For the legend, we'll reuse the same concept we applied to the voting districts: the winning candidate's color is overlaid with a semi-transparent black layer which depends on the voter density.

The first step is to add two rectangles styled using the candidate colors, red and blue. Use the Width and Height input fields in the Position and size section to make sure the height of each rectangle equals twice the width, e.g. 20 x 40 mm as shown in Figure 3.1. This will give us a nice, square legend graphic.

Once you have the base colors in place, we can add another rectangle on top and style it with a transparent to black gradient fill. Figure 3.2, on the next page shows the details of the rectangle gradient style: All we need to change are the Two color inputs—use the defaults for everything else.

To finish the legend, we place explanatory labels with the candidate names as well as the voter density values. As shown in Figure 3.3, on the following page, we can rotate labels by 270° in order to make the text flow upwards.

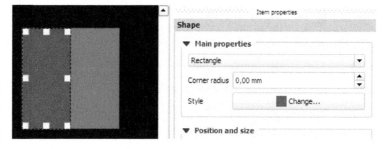

Figure 3.1: Two rectangles in red and blue form the base of our legend graphics

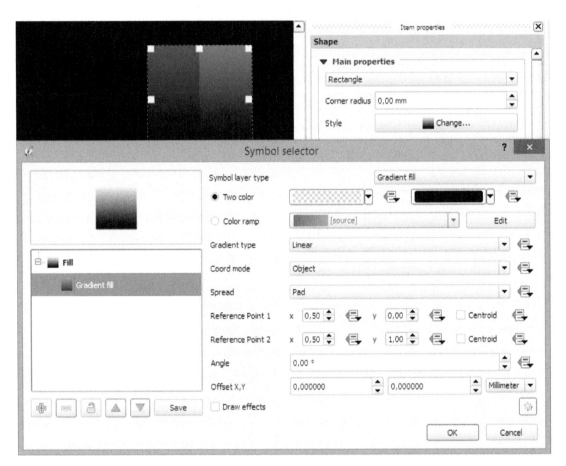

Figure 3.2: A square rectangle with a transparent to black gradient is added next

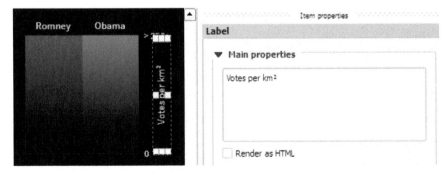

Figure 3.3: Add labels to explain the legend

3.2 Double Gradient Legend

The second version of the map shows how the votes were split between the two leading candidates. The district color changes gradually from red to pink to blue depending on the vote distribution. The color expression used to style the districts is:

```
color_hsl(
  scale_linear( 1.0*"BARACK OBA" /
                ("MITT ROMNE" + "BARACK OBA" )
  ,0.1,0.9,360,240)
  ,100,50)
```

The legend for this map consists of two square rectangles on top of each other. Figure 3.4 shows the square with our color gradient running from right to left. This is achieved by adjusting the Reference Points which control where—with respect to our rectangle—the gradient starts and where it ends.

By setting Reference Point 1 to x = 1 and y = 1, we set the gradient to start in the lower right corner, while Reference Point 2 x = 0 and y = 1 defines the end of the gradient to be in the lower left corner. This makes the gradient run from the right to the left side.

The gradient itself is a custom color ramp with three intermediate stops as shown in Figure 3.5, on the following page.

The black gradient as well as the labels are then added in the same way as in the first legend version. Figure 3.6, on the next page shows the final legend.

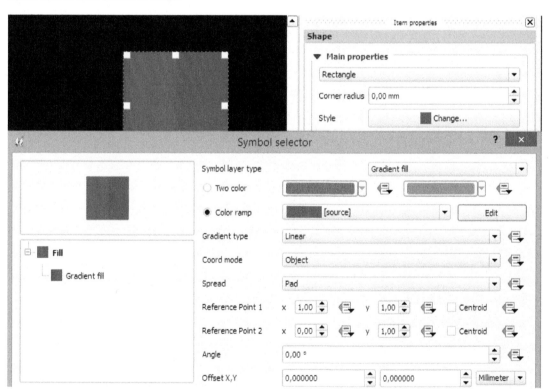

Figure 3.4: A square rectangle with a custom horizontal fill

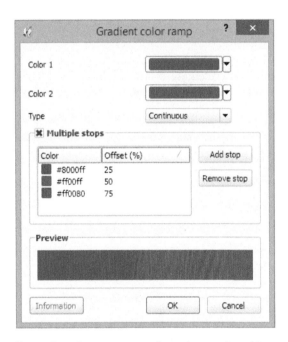

Figure 3.5: Our custom gradient changes from blue to pink to red

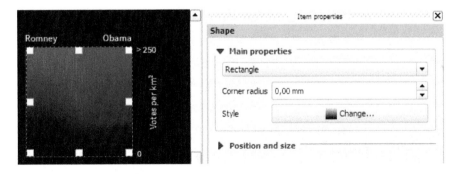

Figure 3.6: Add a transparent to black gradient rectangle and labels to finish the legend

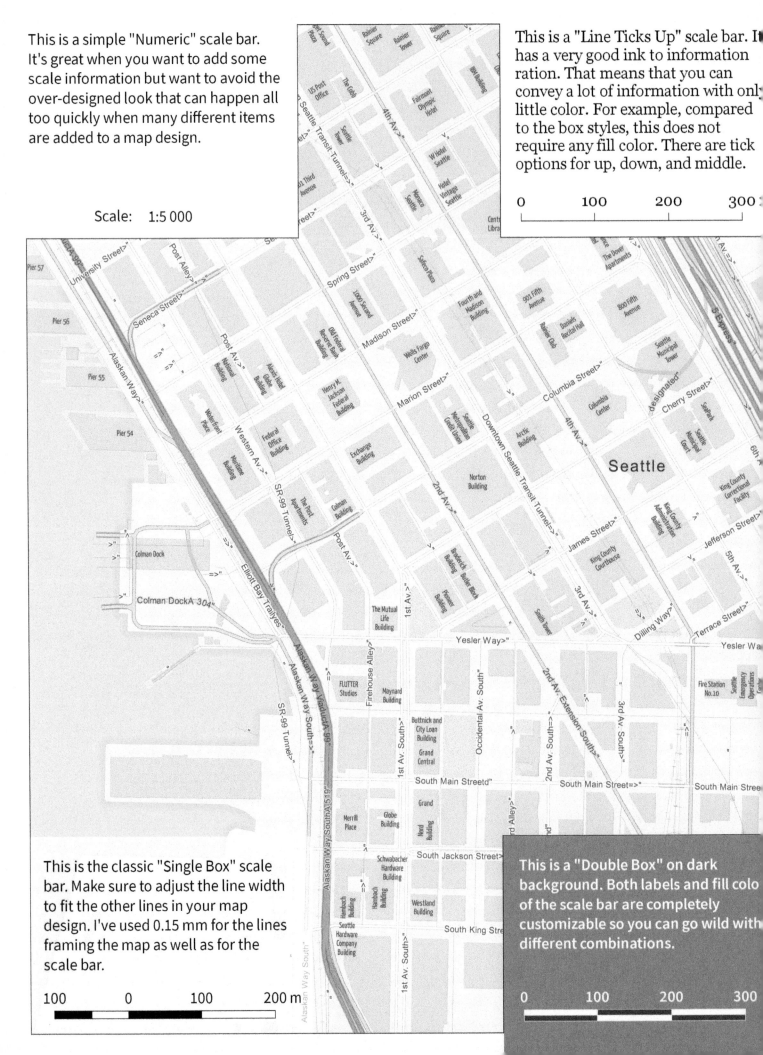

This is a simple "Numeric" scale bar. It's great when you want to add some scale information but want to avoid the over-designed look that can happen all too quickly when many different items are added to a map design.

Scale: 1:5 000

This is a "Line Ticks Up" scale bar. It has a very good ink to information ration. That means that you can convey a lot of information with only little color. For example, compared to the box styles, this does not require any fill color. There are tick options for up, down, and middle.

0   100   200   300

This is the classic "Single Box" scale bar. Make sure to adjust the line width to fit the other lines in your map design. I've used 0.15 mm for the lines framing the map as well as for the scale bar.

100   0   100   200 m

This is a "Double Box" on dark background. Both labels and fill color of the scale bar are completely customizable so you can go wild with different combinations.

0   100   200   300

In this recipe, we rid ourselves of lame default scalebar styles and create four different aesthetically pleasing scalebars for our print maps.

> To reproduce this map in QGIS, open the scalebars.qgs project.

4.1 Numeric Scalebar

The simplest scalebar we can add to a map is a Numeric scale bar. Select the Add new scalebar tool (see Figure 4.1) and click on the page location where you want to add the scalebar.

Figure 4.1: The add new scalebar tool

By default, this will add a Single box scalebar. To switch to a numeric style, we open the Item properties and change the Style in the Main properties section to Numeric as shown in Figure 4.2. The remaining configuration options for this style are rather limited. You might want to adjust the Fonts and colors in the corresponding section further down in the Item properties panel.

4.2 Reduced Line Scalebar

If you are looking for an actual scalebar but prefer a very reduced style, the Line Ticks styles are a good option. In this recipe, we use the Line Ticks Up style. By default, there is quite a lot going on: two segments on the left side, and four on the right. Figure 4.3 shows the scalebar default design on top and the cleaned up design we want to achieve on the bottom.

In Figure 4.4, on the next page, you can see all the settings necessary to improve the design. First, we reduce the number of segments

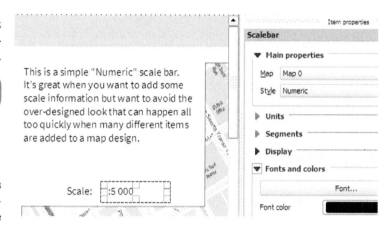

Figure 4.2: The numeric style simply displays the scale values

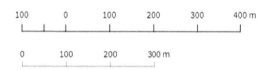

Figure 4.3: Default line ticks up style (top) and our design (bottom)

to none on the left and 3 on the right. We also reduce the Height of the vertical segment lines to 2 mm. In the Display section, we then reduce the Line width to, for example, 0.15 mm. Finally, we reduce the gap between lines and labels by setting the Labels margin to 2.00 mm.

Of course, we can also change the scalebar font. For this example, we chose Georgia in the scalebar item's Fonts and color section.

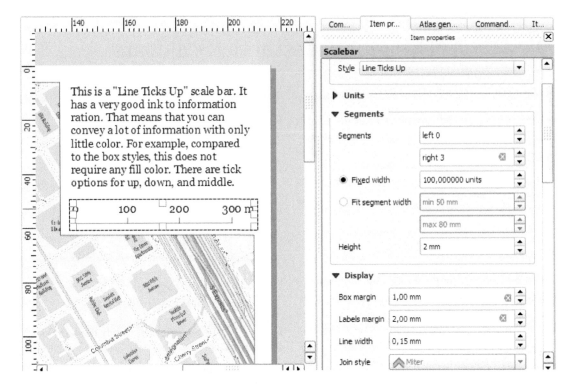

Figure 4.4: Line ticks are a good solution for visually unobstrusive scalebars

4.3   Classic Single Box Scalebar

The Single Box style is the classic scalebar look. In this example, we will make use of those segments on the left-hand side of zero, as shown in Figure 4.5.

Figure 4.5: Default single box style (top) and our design (bottom)

As you can see in Figure 4.6, on the next page, we increase the number of segments on the left to 5 in order to get 20 meter wide segments. Otherwise, we use the same settings which we used to improve the Line Ticks style.

This example also shows that you don't necessarily need a completely opaque background for the scalebar. If the map section where you want to put the scalebar is not too busy, you can also get away with a semi-transparent background.

4.4   Double Box on Dark Background

Of course not all maps have a white or light background, that's where the customization options in the Fonts and colors section come in handy. For example, Figure 4.7, on the facing page shows the default Double Box style which—besides the previously discussed design issues—also suffers from quite bad contrast with the background.

To solve this issue, we can switch all black color settings to white and the previously white Secondary fill color to dark gray as shown in Figure 4.8, on page 162.

Since light fonts can be a bit hard to read, you might want to use bolder fonts, such as Source Sans Pro Semibold shown in this example.

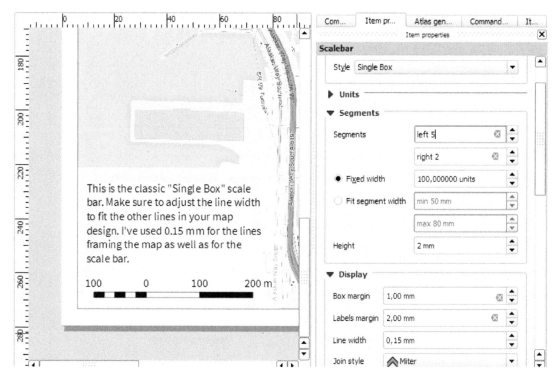

Figure 4.6: Settings for the single box style

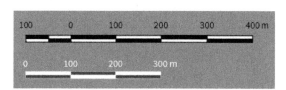

Figure 4.7: Default double box style (top) and our design (bottom)

To fine tune the placement of these rectangles, zoom in close to the corners where the original map border and the black lines of our rectangle style meet. Now you can use the mouse or hold down `Alt` and use the arrow keys on your keyboard to move the rectangle into the perfect position.

You can use the mouse wheel to zoom.

4.5 Bonus: Corner Cutouts

If you had a closer look at the map at the beginning of this recipe, you have probably noticed the corner cutouts. These cutouts are simple rectangle shapes which have been placed on top of the map. To create the illusion of the map border following the cutout shape, we customize the rectangle **Style** as shown in Figure 4.9, on page 163. The trick is to add a second symbol layer in black (the color of the map border) and shift it a little by applying offsets in the x and y direction. For the upper left corner cutout, the offsets are `0.15` in x and `0.15` in y direction. For the upper right corner, we use `-0.15` in x and `0.15`. And so on for the other corners.

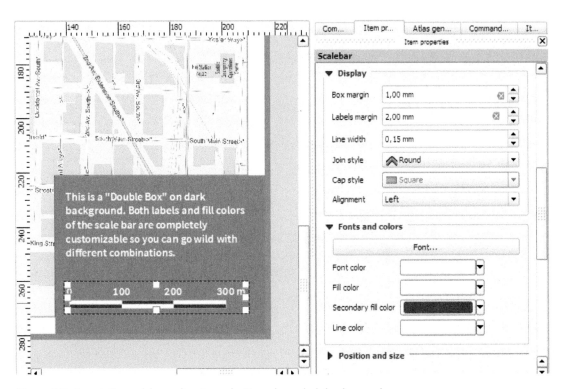

Figure 4.8: Invert the scalebar colors to make it work on dark backgrounds

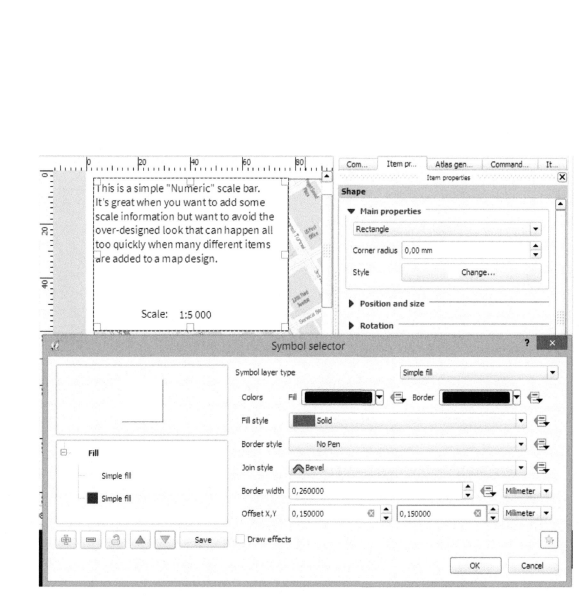

Figure 4.9: The offset values are same as the map border width

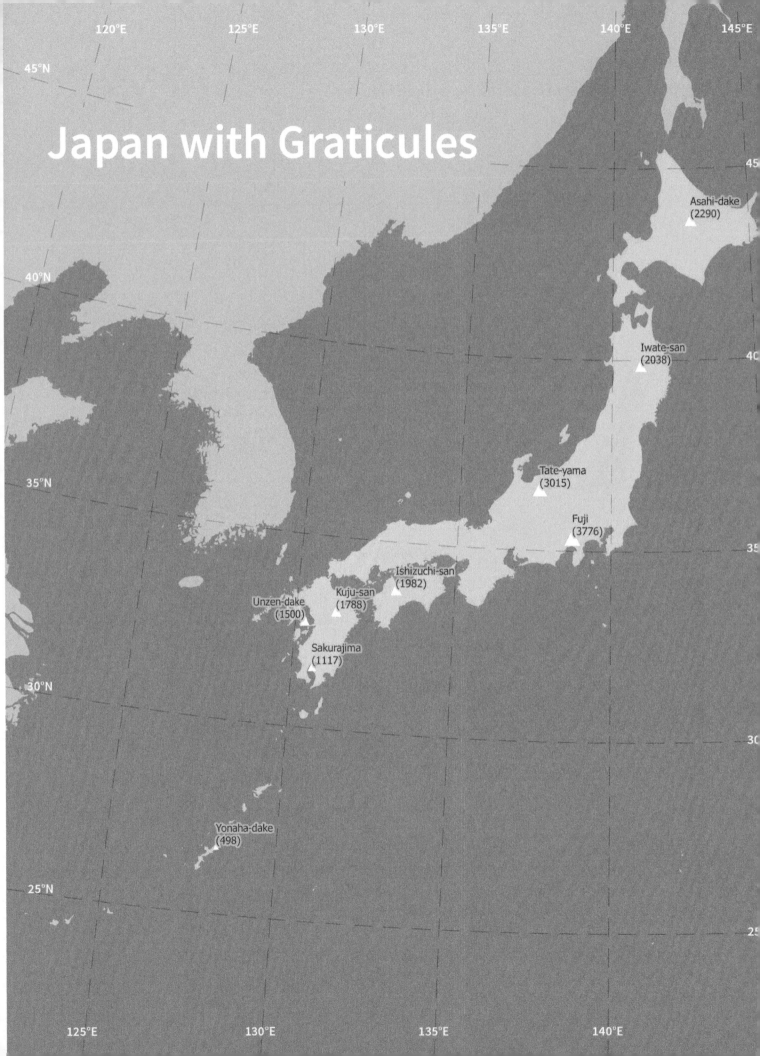

Japan with Graticules

Asahi-dake
(2290)

Iwate-san
(2038)

Tate-yama
(3015)

Fuji
(3776)

Ishizuchi-san
(1982)

Kuju-san
(1788)

Unzen-dake
(1500)

Sakurajima
(1117)

Yonaha-dake
(498)

5. Graticules for Regional Maps

In this recipe, we create a subtle latitude and longitude grid for our map of Japan. The grid formed by latitude and longitude is also known as a *graticule*.

> To reproduce this map in QGIS, open the graticules.qgs project.

5.1 Adding a Latitude/Longitude Grid

Select the map item and scroll to the **Grids** section in the **Item properties**. Press the button with the green plus to add a grid to the list. Before anything gets displayed on the map, we need to configure the grid. Our project uses the "Tokyo / UTM zone 54N" projection. To create a latitude/longitude grid, we need to change the CRS to EPSG:4326 as shown in Figure 5.1. We also specify an **Interval** of 5 degrees for both the x and the y direction.

To create dashed grid lines rather than solid lines, we change the **Line style** and specify a custom dash pattern with dash length 5 and space length 3. The line color is #bab6af and the width 0.2. Finally, we set the **Blend mode** to **Multiply**.

5.2 Adding Coordinates to the Grid

To add coordinate information to our grid, we need to scroll down to the **Draw coordinates** section and enable the corresponding option. Figure 5.2 shows the default coordinate labels in black as well as the label styling we are aiming for in white.

Figure 5.3, on the next page shows the settings for our grid coordinate labels. The first thing to change is the **Format** which defaults to **Decimal**. By switching to **Decimal with suffix**, we add the degree symbol as well as the geographic direction. At the same time, we can

Figure 5.1: Multiple grids with different CRS and interval settings can be added to the same map

The interval unit is measured in degrees because we changed the CRS to EPSG:4326.

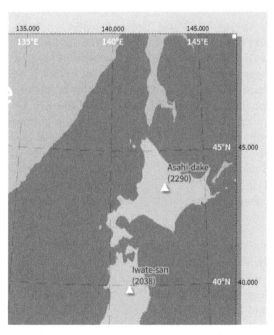

Figure 5.2: Default coordinate style in black and our customized style in white

also decrease the Coordinate precision to 0 since we are only drawing grid lines in 5 degree intervals anyway.

Figure 5.3: Customize the coordinate settings

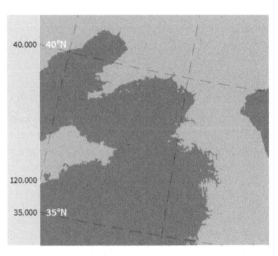

Figure 5.4: Latitute only removes the 120 degree label from the left side of the frame border

5.3 Adding a second grid

As mentioned above, it is possible to add multiple grids to the same map. These grids can have different CRS or simply different line styles or coordinate label settings. Figure 5.5, on the next page shows an example where we add a second grid with 1 degree spacing and without coordinate labels.

In the middle of the Draw coordinates section, there is a long list of dropdowns which allow us to control the labels on each side of the grid separately. For each side, we can decide if we want to Show all labels or only show latitude or longitude. Figure 5.4 shows the difference between Show all (black labels) and Show latitude only (white labels) for the left side. Note how the 120 degree east grid line is only labeled if Show all is selected. Removing the 120 degree longitude label restores the equal spacing between labels and is less confusing for the map reader.

Finally, since we want the grid labels to appear on top of the map, we change the position for each side from Outside frame to Inside frame and increase the Distance to map frame to 6 mm to add some more space between the grid labels and the edge of our map.

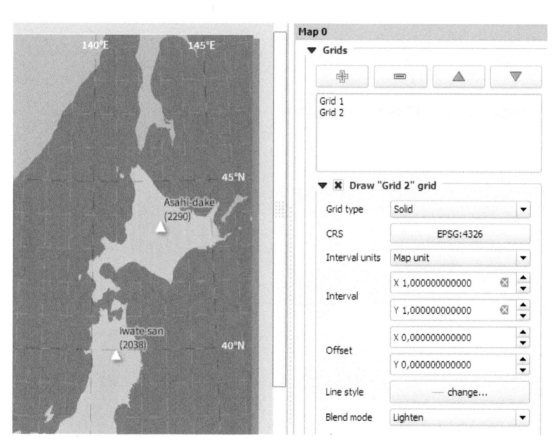

Figure 5.5: A second unlabeled grid can add more detail

North America

map area

Canyonlands

Capitol
Reef

Glen
Canyon

Zion

Grand
Canyon

Lake
Mead

El
Malpais

White
Sands
NM

Petrified
Forest

Mojave

Death
Valley

Joshua
Tree

Yosemite

Kings
Canyon

Sequoia

Santa
Monica
Mountains

Channel
Islands

Overview maps are generally placed in insets on the main layout. They show a zoomed-out view of the mapped area in order to put it in geographic context. Usually, overview maps are styled more simply than the main map, though overview maps with the exact styling of the main map are sometimes helpful. In this recipe we'll create an overview map that uses a shapeburst fill and a dynamic rectangle to indicate where the main map is on the overview.

> To reproduce this map in QGIS, begin with the finished map from the Placing Labels By Hand For Small Area Features recipe, which can be found in the `handplaced_labels.qgs` project. Alternatively, view this finished recipe in the `overview_maps.qgs` project.

6.1 Add Data to the National Parks Map

Add the parks and protected lands shapefile (`ne_10m_parks_and_protected_lands_area_labels.shp`) to the project and copy and paste the styling from the old labels layer to this one, then delete the old labels layer. These labels are placed in the right position for the size and shape of the layout page that we'll create. The new labels may appear a bit far away from the features in the project at this point, which is okay.

We also want to add a few more details onto the main map, so add the following layers as well:

```
ne_10m_admin_1_states_provinces
ne_10m_admin_0_countries
```

The states are styled with no fill, a border width of 0.5 millimeters, and a border color of #b0c8aa. The states layer is placed just above the raster. The countries layer is styled with a transparent fill and default-width black border. It is placed above the other layers. This completes the main map set up.

6.2 Style the Inset Map Layers

The inset map will be a very simple map of the North America landmass in light brown with a white shapeburst around it. Inset maps are commonly framed with heavy black borders which cause undue visual emphasis. In this recipe, a more seamless appearance is achieved with the shapeburst effect, which still provides the needed visual separation but is tied directly to the geography as shown in Figure 6.1.

Figure 6.1: Inset map with shapeburst fill

The inset map has only two layers to keep it simple. To begin, duplicate the countries layer, rename it Americas, style it with a fill color of #edece1 and no border. Also filter it in the Provider feature filter with the following:

```
"SUBREGION" IN ('Central America',
                'Northern America')
```

Duplicate the Americas layer and put both the duplicated copy and the original Americas layer into their own grouped layer (not a sub-group layer) named inset. At this point your project should have a group layer ("main map") for the main map layers and a group layer ("inset") for the inset map layers.

The copied layer will have the same feature filter but be styled with the inverted polygons render and shapeburst fill. Use a two-color shapeburst going from white to transparent and shaded to a distance of 3 millimeters. Optionally, check the Merge polygons before rendering box to ensure that the country borders aren't visible. However, this slows down the rendering considerably. Rename it Shapeburst and place it above the Americas layer in the inset group. Turn off the inset group and leave the main map subgroup visible.

You may also want to explore using Visibility Presets to preset the map views.

Now, here's where it can get tricky if we don't set things up right. Because the inset will have a different scale than the main map, make sure to set a bookmark for the main map scale so you can easily return to it. Do that now before changing the scale in the next steps.

6.3 Page Layout

In this section we'll create the small layout that will showcase the Southwest U.S. national parks map and its accompanying overview map inset. The size of the finished layout makes it ideal for a slide show, in-line report graphic, or magazine figure.

Begin by opening a new print composer (we've called ours "overview") and set the page size to 4.5" by 3.0". Turn Snap to grid on and add the main map to the full size of the page as shown in Figure 6.2.

Now, here is the key to adding another map to the same composer window: lock the layers for this map before adding the overview map. Notice that when the map is active in the print composer that the Item properties, Main properties section has a toggle for Lock layers for map item. You'll want to make sure this is checked on as shown in Figure 6.3, on the facing page.

Once that's clicked, the Lock layer styles for map item toggle becomes available. Check to enable the lock layer styles as well. This map that we just added to the print composer is now locked and will not change when the map in

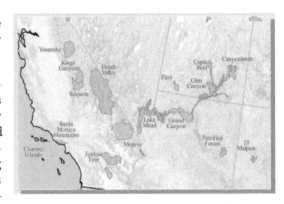

Figure 6.2: Add the main map to the new print composer layout

the project is changed.

Back in the project window, turn on the inset group layers and turn off the main map group layers. Zoom out so that Canada, U.S., and Central America are all visible. This zoom extent will likely need to be adjusted in a future step but is sufficient for now.

Switch to the print composer window and add a new map to the layout, placed in the upper-right corner. This map will display whatever is visible in the project window, which in this case is the simple Americas map. See Figure 6.4, on the next page.

You may need to tweak the map in the main project to get it to the right scale and location. If you need to adjust the other map at this point, lock the layers and styles for map item 1 (i.e., inset), unlock the layers and styles for map item 0 (i.e., main map) and make your changes.

6.4 The Overview Locator

With the dynamic overview capabilities of QGIS, there is no need to hand-draw area locators—they're created automatically. To do this with our map, make sure that Map 1 is active in the print composer and click the Item properties, Overviews add button. Set the map frame to Map 0 and change its style to whatever is desired. This is shown in Figure 6.5, on page 172.

Add a label for North America and for the map area and the layout is complete. The final map

Figure 6.3: The lock layers functionality is very important when there are multiple maps on the same layout

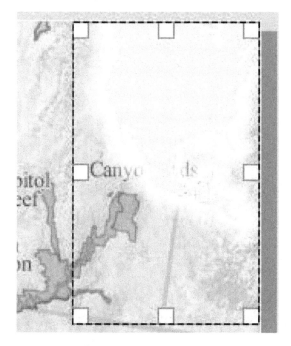

Figure 6.4: Adding the inset map to the corner of the layout

is shown at the beginning of this recipe.

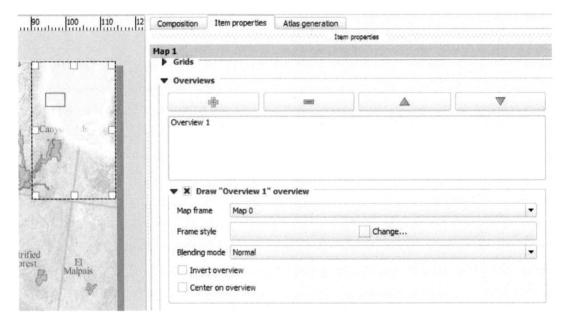

Figure 6.5: Create the dynamic overview indicator box in the Overviews property

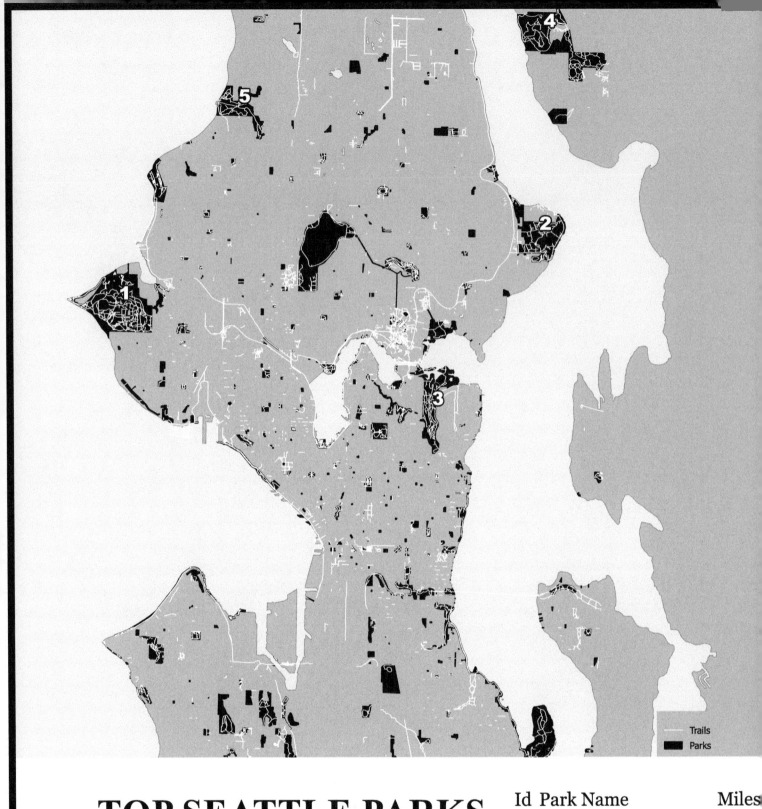

TOP SEATTLE PARKS
by
TRAIL LENGTH

0   1 mile

Trails
Parks

Id	Park Name	Miles
1	Discovery Park	22.21
2	Warren G. Magnuson Park	9.81
3	Washington Park Arboretum	8.61
4	Saint Edward State Park	7.42
5	Carkeek Park	5.36
6	Green Lake Park	5.04
7	Big Finn Hill Park	4.82
8	Seward Park	4.05
9	Ravenna Park	3.78
10	Golden Gardens Park	3.3

7. Attribute Tables in Layouts, Seattle Parks Map

In this recipe, we'll create a monochromatic map of Seattle parks with the longest trails. The map will be small, as for inclusion in a report. The recipe guides us through the creation of a highly formatted attribute table that provides the name and total mileage of each of the top parks as well as identification numbers for locating them on the map.

While this recipe includes the specifics for formatting a smaller report map, the project file accompanying the recipe contains two print composer layouts, one for the smaller map and one for the larger one shown at the beginning of this recipe.

> To reproduce this map in QGIS, open the attribute_tables.qgs project.

7.1 Setting up the Base Layers

Set up the water and land base layers by adding the multipolygons table from the `seattle_osm.db` database with the following query:

```
"natural" = "water"
```

Make a duplicate of that layer and symbolize the duplicate with the inverted polygon renderer. This will be the land. Name each layer accordingly and symbolize the water with a light gray hue and the land with a medium gray hue.

The parks and paths both come from the same database, but with more complex queries. A close examination of the line data indicates that there are several "path-like" attributes in the highway field. The following expression will capture them all:

```
"highway" = 'cycleway' OR
"highway" = 'footway' OR
"highway" = 'path' OR
"highway" = 'pedestrian' OR
"highway" = 'social_path' OR
"highway" = 'steps'
```

Name this layer and symbolize it with a thin white line. Add another seattle_osm database connection for the parks. The parks come from the multipolygons table and are queried with the following expression:

```
"leisure" = 'park' OR
"leisure" = 'nature_reserve'
```

Change the project CRS to `EPSG:102348` (NAD 1983 HARN StatePlane Washington North). Since the projection's units are in meters, the output of the analysis we'll do in the next section will be in meters.

> If the CRS were WGS84, the default, then the output of the analysis in the next section would be in degrees and not very helpful.

7.2 Path Mileage Analysis

The lengths of the path lines need to be added together within each of the parks. Use the Vector, Analysis Tools, Sum Line Lengths tool to do this. The input polygon vector layer is the parks layer, the input line vector layer is the paths layer, the output summed length field name is `lengthM`, and the output shapefile is `PathLength`. (Note there is already a `PathLength` shapefile in the resources folder for the example project—rename as needed.)

Running this tool gives us the length in meters, per park, in a field called `lengthM`. Create a new field in the `PathLength` table to contain the lengths in miles as well as to confine the precision to two decimal places. To do this, create a field called `lengthMi` to contain real numbers, a width of 4, and a precision of 2. In the field calculator divide lengthM by 1609.34 to convert to miles in the `lengthMi` field.

The finished map will use identification numbers to identify the parks in the accompanying data table. To do this, add a field called `IdNum`, click the `lengthMi` field twice to order the table so that the parks with the longest path lengths are at the top, and manually enter in the first 5 or 10 ID numbers. Make sure to save the edits. Our sample data has identification numbers assigned to the top 10 parks for the larger map layout shown at the beginning of this recipe.

Style the PathLength layer black with a matching black border to help the smaller parks standout. Label the PathLength layer with the `IdNum` field, using Arial Black, size 14, white and a black text buffer of size 0.7 millimeters. The text buffer is necessary to enable these numbers to be really visible against the monochromatic background. For placement, set the labels to `Around centroid`.

7.3   Creating a Layout With an Attribute Table

Create a new print composer layout named `pathsmap` and set the size of the page to 3" by 5". Add a black border to the page and then place the map so that it covers about the top 2/3 of the page. The bottom third of the page will contain the title, scale bar, and attribute table.

Create a legend as shown in the final map in Figure 7.1. Place it over a gray part of the map. It may be necessary to match the legend background with the gray land color so that the white path legend item sufficiently contrasts. We've also changed the legend item names from paths to Trails and from PathLength to Parks and aren't including the land or water legend entries. Add a title and simple scale bar.

Place an attribute table using the **Add attribute table** tool in the lower-right portion of the page. If the attribute table's **Item properties, Layer** isn't set to the PathLength layer, do so.

All the fields from the dataset will be shown by default, whereas we want to show only three. To remedy this, click the **Item properties, Attributes...** button and modify the fields that are shown in the **Select attributes** dialog. The

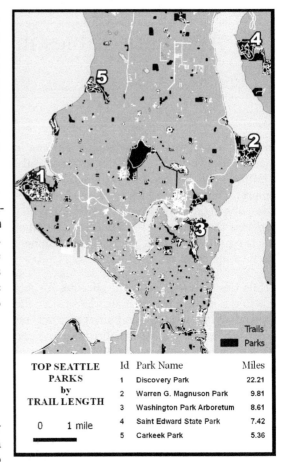

Figure 7.1: The map in its final form

dialog will originally appear as shown in Figure 7.2, on the facing page.

The top section of this dialog shows all the columns (fields) in the layer's attribute table. We only want to display the name, `lengthMi`, and `IdNum` fields on the page so delete all the others using the red minus sign button. It should now look like Figure 7.3, on the next page.

If we left the **Columns** section as-is and clicked OK the table would appear as shown in Figure 7.4, on the facing page, but there are several things wrong. The headings aren't ideal, the wrong parks are listed, the order isn't right, and the grid is too heavy looking.

As seen in Figure 7.5, on the next page, the headings can be changed in the **Select attributes** dialog.

name	lengthMi	IdNum
Richmond Beach Saltwater Park	0.89	
Ravenna Boulevard Park	0	
Banner Way Triangles	0	

Figure 7.4: The attribute table with the correct fields but incorrect rows and styling

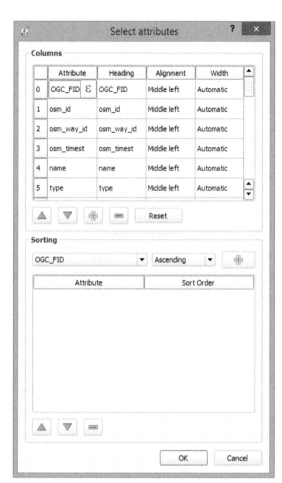

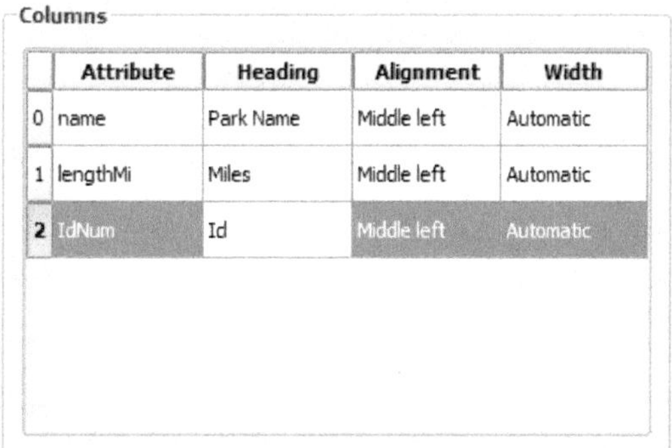

Figure 7.2: The select attributes dialog

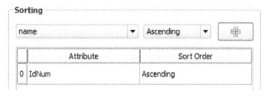

Figure 7.5: To change the headings, simply type in the headings column

Move the `IdNum` attribute to the top of the list so it will show first in the table. Highlight its row in the list and use the up triangle button for this. Change the **Alignment** for the `lengthMi` attribute to Middle right.

In the **Sorting** section of the **Select attributes** dialog change the first drop-down to `IdNum` and change the second drop-down to `Ascending` and click the green plus button to make sure that this setting gets saved as shown in Figure 7.6.

Figure 7.6: Specify how the table should be sorted in the sorting section

The correct parks are still not visible in the table, so to fix that we'll filter the attribute table so that it only shows rows with an ID less than or equal to 5. Use the **Item properties**, **Feature filtering** section to specify this filter as shown in Figure 7.7, on the next page. If the resulting table doesn't show all five parks, the table area probably needs to be lengthened so they become visible.

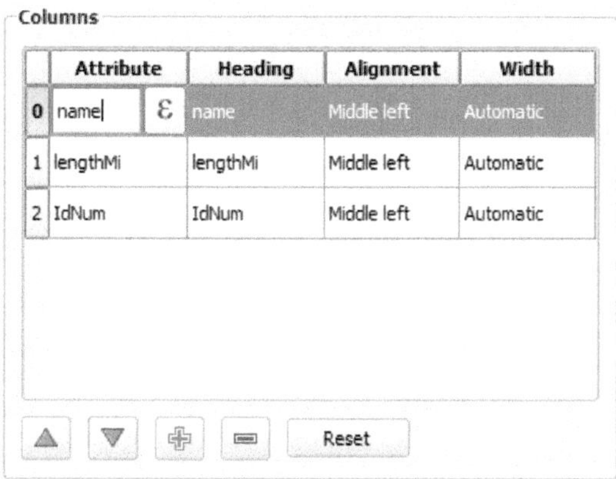

Figure 7.3: The attributes pared down to the three that we'd like to show on the layout

Figure 7.7: Feature filter settings for the attribute table

The data inside attribute tables is hard to read when its inside dark black cell outlines. For this map we want to delete the grid entirely to make the data easier to read. To do that, disable the Item properties, Show grid setting.

Finally, change the heading font to Georgia 8 pt and the table contents font to Arial 6 pt in the Item properties, Fonts and text styling settings. The attribute table now appears as shown in Figure 7.8. Move it so that it is situated nicely within the layout and the map is done.

Id	Park Name	Miles
1	Discovery Park	22.21
2	Warren G. Magnuson Park	9.81
3	Washington Park Arboretum	8.61
4	Saint Edward State Park	7.42
5	Carkeek Park	5.36

Figure 7.8: The attribute table in its final form

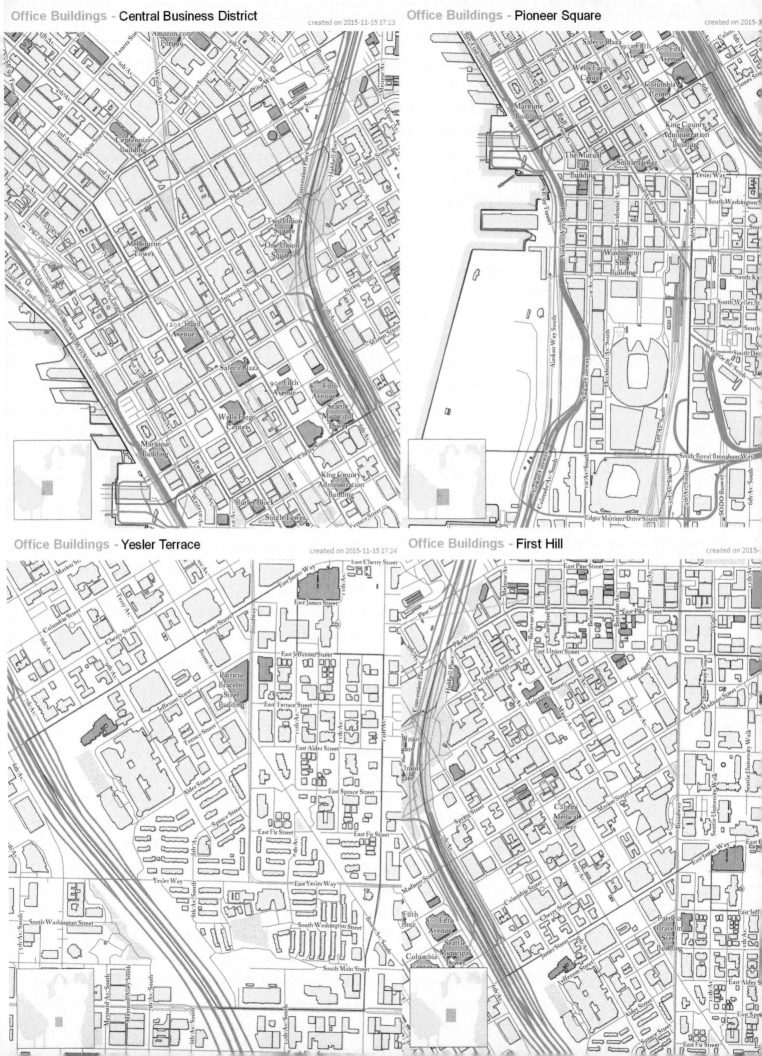

Office Buildings - Central Business District
created on 2015-11-15 17:23

Office Buildings - Pioneer Square
created on 2015-

Office Buildings - Yesler Terrace
created on 2015-11-15 17:24

Office Buildings - First Hill
created on 2015-

8. Map Series with Atlas

In this recipe, we'll create a series of maps. Each map features a different neighborhood of Seattle. This style is inspired by the 1920 Sanborn fire insurance map of sugar warehouses in Cienfuegos, Cuba[21].

> To reproduce this map in QGIS, open the `map_series.qgs` project. Our map uses a new font called Fanwood which you can also find in the resources folder.

8.1 Setting Up the Map Series

To set up a map series in the Print Composer we need to do two things: configure the map item which will be controlled by the Atlas and configure the Atlas itself.

To configure the map item, we activate the **Controlled by atlas** section in the map's **Item properties**. As shown in Figure 8.1, we use the flexible **Margin around feature** option in this recipe. This setting makes sure that map will zoom to accommodate the feature (in our case neighborhoods) plus **10%** margin. The other options are: **Predefined scale** which selects the most appropriate scale from the scales defined in the QGIS options (`Settings->Options`) and **Fixed scale** which always uses the scale defined for the map item.

To configure the Atlas itself, we switch to the **Atlas generation** tab. Here, we first need to activate the **Generate an atlas** option. Then we can specify that we want the Atlas to create one map per neighborhood by setting the **Coverage layer** to seattle_neighborhoods. In addition, we can limit our map series to certain neighborhoods by applying a filter. In this recipe we activate the **Filter with** option to only create maps for neighborhoods, which match the expression `"NEIGHUM" in (6,51,96,114)` as shown in Figure 8.2. This limits our Atlas to the neighborhoods First Hill, Yesler Terrace, Pioneer Square, and Central Business District.

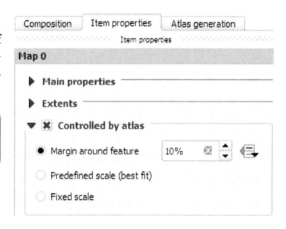

Figure 8.1: Set up the map for Atlas control

Figure 8.2: Configuring the Atlas

You can see the Atlas in action by activating the **Preview Atlas** functionality in the **Atlas** toolbar as shown in Figure 8.3, on the next page. The arrows in this toolbar allow you to switch between the different pages of the map series. Here you also find the buttons to export the Atlas to images, PDFs or SVGs.

If you use the normal export buttons, they will only export the currently viewed map instead of the whole series.

21. `http://loc8.cc/qmd/fire_ins`

Figure 8.3: Activate and navigate through the Atlas preview using the Atlas toolbar buttons

8.2   Dynamic Titles

Once the basic map series is configured, we can move on to the details, such as automatically updating map titles. This is another nice feature which makes use of the `@atlas_feature` variable which is one of multiple Atlas-related variables you can find in the expression builder as shown in Figure 8.4.

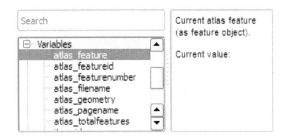

Figure 8.4: Atlas variables provide access to different information about the map series

To insert a label which shows the neighborhood name, we use the expression:

```
[% "NEIGHBORHO" %]
```

as shown in Figure 8.5. This expression returns the value of the `'NEIGHBORHO'` variable (which contains the name) of the current Atlas feature.

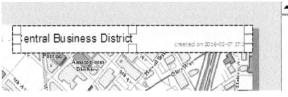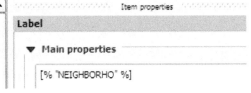

Figure 8.5: This map title updates dynamically

There's also a second dynamic label on these maps which shows the timestamp of the map creation. To achieve this, we use the `now()` function which returns the current timestamp. As shown in Figure 8.6, on the facing page, we can apply different formats to the timestamp to create the output we prefer.

8.3   Overview maps in map series

For map series, a design decision we find often is to show an overview map of the same extent on each page. Therefore, we do not activate the Atlas control for the map item which serves as the overview as you can see in Figure 8.7, on the next page. The map itself is really simple and only shows the water polygon features below the rectangle which marks the area of interest.

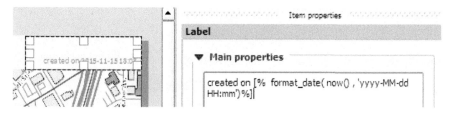

Figure 8.6: Add a custom dynamically updating timestamp to the map

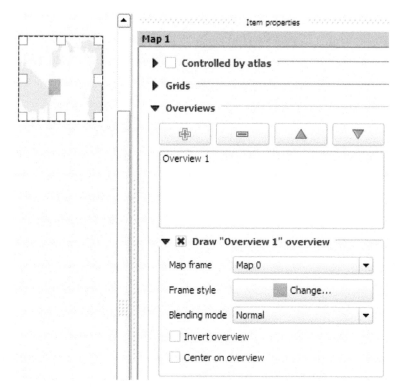

Figure 8.7: The overview extent should be same on all maps

8.4 Highlighting the current map feature

Last but not least, we will highlight the current neighborhood feature. In this recipe, we use a simple red outline to delineate the neighborhood. This can be achieved, for example, using a rule-based style as shown in Figure 8.8 for the neighborhood layer. The rule:

```
@atlas_featureid = $id
```

makes sure that only the feature whose ID is equal to the ID of the current Atlas feature is drawn.

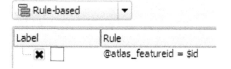

Figure 8.8: This rule only draws the current Atlas feature

Mountains of Japan

- Fuji
- Tate-yama
- Asahi-dake
- Iwate-san
- Ishizuchi-san
- Kuju-san
- Unzen-dake
- Sakurajima
- Yonahe-dake

Asahi-dake
(2290)

Iwate-san
(2038)

Tate-yama
(3015)

Fuji
(3776)

Ishizuchi-san
(1982)

Kuju-san
(1788)

Unzen-dake
(1500)

Sakurajima
(1117)

Yonaha-dake
(498)

9. Designing Infographics

In this recipe, we'll create an infographic in the Print Composer using HTML and CSS. The technique presented in this recipe is a convenient way to add simple and customizable bar graphs to a map without having to leave QGIS. Alternative approaches often involve preparing the diagrams in an external application such as Inkscape and then embedding them as images.

> To reproduce this map in QGIS, open the infographics_japan.qgs project. The background image we use for this recipe is Mt. Fuji by TANAKA Juuyoh (on Flickr) under CC BY 2.0 license.

9.1 Setting Up the Map

The first step is to add the background image. We already added images in the Seattle coffee map recipe and the Curved area labels recipe. The process is simple, we just need a picture item. In the picture's Item properties panel, we can pick the Image source file fuji.jpg from the book resources folder. Resize the picture item to cover the whole page as shown in Figure 9.1, on the next page. You can temporarily increase the Transparency in the Rendering section to make the picture transparent enough to see the page below.

On top of the picture item, we can now add the map item as shown in Figure 9.2, on the following page. We mostly use the nice blue sky of the background image to provide contrast for our land areas but if you look closely, some of the southern islands also end up on the slopes of the mountain, but that's fine.

9.2 Creating the Infographics

With the background and map in place, there is a nice empty space in the top left corner which we will use for our diagram. Of course we could simply add an image of a diagram and be done with it but where would be the fun in

that? Instead, we will create a diagram using HTML and CSS. To be able to use HTML and CSS, we need to add a label item and activate the Render as HTML option as shown in Figure 9.3, on page 187.

The full HTML markup for the diagram in this recipe is:

```html
<html>
 <head>
  <style language="html/css">
  .bargraph {
   list-style: none;
   padding-left: 0px;
   width: 560px;
  }
  ul.bargraph li {
   height: 35px;
   color: #333;
   text-align: left;
   font-family: Source Sans Pro, Sans;
   font-size: 10pt;
   line-height: 35px;
   padding: 0px 20px;
   margin-bottom: 5px;
   background: #f0f0f0;
  }
  </style>
 </head>
<body>
 <ul class="bargraph">
 <li style="width:407px">Fuji</li>
 <li style="width:332px">Tate-yama</li>
 <li style="width:259px">Asahi-dake</li>
 <li style="width:234px">Iwate-san</li>
 <li style="width:228px">Ishizuchi-san</li>
 <li style="width:209px">Kuju-san</li>
 <li style="width:180px">Unzen-dake</li>
 <li style="width:142px">Sakurajima</li>
 <li style="width:80px">Yonahe-dake</li>
 </ul>
 </body>
</html>
```

Explaining HTML and CSS in detail is out of the scope of this book but if you look through the markup, you will quickly see that there is a `<style>` section at the beginning and a content section inside the `<body>`. In the `<style>`

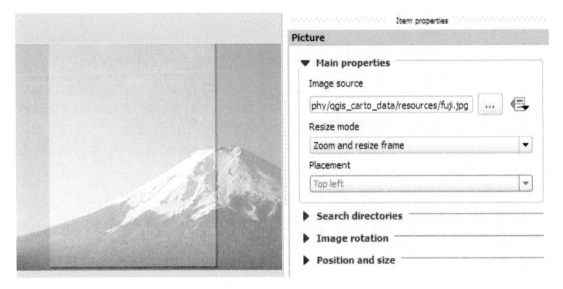

Figure 9.1: The background of our infographic is a picture of Mount Fuji

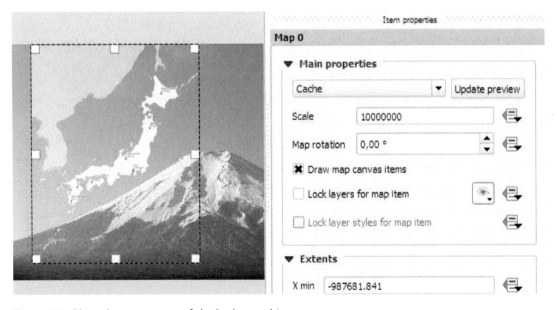

Figure 9.2: Place the map on top of the background image

Figure 9.3: You can use HTML and CSS markup in label items

section, you can customize the look of the diagram, including colors, sizes, and the font used for labeling. In the <body> section, we then create the graph—one bar at a time.

The width of the bars for this recipe was computed based on the corresponding mountain's elevation using elevation / 10 + 30. It's necessary to add 30 pixels to the width to make sure that the label of the lowest mountain, Yonahadake, still fits into the corresponding bar.

9.3 Finishing Touches

To finish the infographics, we add a label item for the title and one for the image credits. Many infographics will contain further text blocks which provide additional explanation and interpretation of the depicted data.

GDP per Capita

Lorem ipsum dolor sit amet, consectetur adipiscing elit. Suspendisse et mattis massa. Etiam sollicitudin lobortis quam, vitae molestie lectus congue sit amet. Fusce iaculis tortor ligula, et sollicitudin leo ultrices non. Etiam varius eros augue, vitae luctus mi aliquam sit amet. Duis a erat eros. Sed consectetur vehicula turpis a pharetra. Vestibulum malesuada lectus nec dapibus lacinia.

Lorem ipsum dolor sit amet, consectetur adipiscing elit. Suspendisse et mattis massa. Etiam sollicitudin lobortis quam, vitae molestie lectus congue sit amet.

GDP per capita

<= 5000 $ <= 20000 $
<= 1000 $ <= 10000 $ > 20000 $

Southern Europe

Central America

Caribbean

South Africa

In this recipe, we'll design a map featuring small multiples which display the GDP in different areas of the world. This recipe builds on the style we introduced in Mapping Economies Using GDP Choropleths or Scaled Symbols, on page 31.

> To reproduce this map in QGIS, open the small_multiples.qgs project.

10.1 Arranging the Multiples

This map features four small multiples. Each map item is 100 x 100 mm big (configured in the Position and size section) and rendered using a scale of 37500000 as shown in Figure 10.1. The simplest way to create all four maps is to first insert and configure one of them, then copy and paste it three more times.

Figure 10.1: We use four map items to create the multiples

A very useful Print Composer feature for arranging items, such as small multiples, on a map are the smart guides which can be enabled in View->Smart Guides as shown in Figure 10.2. The smart guide lines snap to the borders of other items on the page, as well as to the page borders.

Even with smart guides, getting the spacing between items correct can be a bit of a challenge. One way to solve this is to use helper rectangles, like the rectangles highlighted in orange in Figure 10.3, on the next page. In this recipe, we use a spacing of 5 mm. Therefore, the vertical helper rectangle is 5 mm wide and the horizontal one is 5 mm high. By arranging the helper rectangles between the map items, it is easy to ensure equal spacing. Once you are happy with the arrangement, you can either color the helper rectangles in black (like our map background) or turn them invisible in the Items tab.

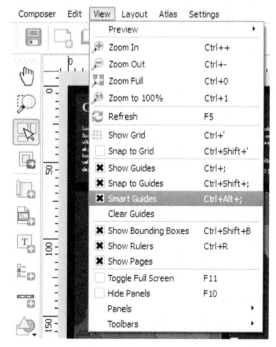

Figure 10.2: Smart guides automatically snap to existing items

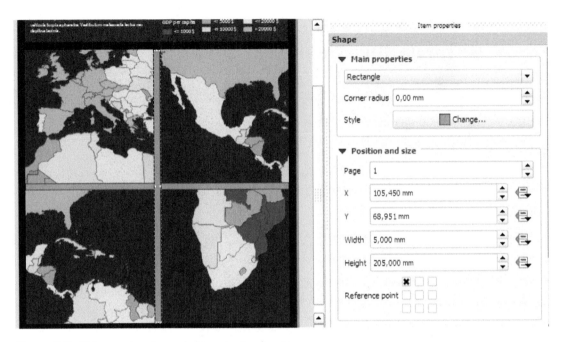

Figure 10.3: Helper rectangles make it easier to align items

10.2   Designing the Masks

To highlight our areas of interest, we add a mask rule to the country layer style. As Figure 10.4 shows, this rule does not need a filter, because it should be applied to all features in the layer.

The mask has to be different for each map item. To achieve this effect, we define the following expression to control the mask symbol's fill color:

```
CASE
 WHEN @map_id = 'canvas'
 THEN color_rgba(0,0,0,0)
 WHEN @map_id = "SUBREGION"
 THEN color_rgba(0,0,0,0)
 ELSE color_rgba(0,0,0,130)
END
```

The @map_id variable gives us access to the id of the individual map items. For the map in the main application window, @map_id equals 'canvas'. In this case, we set the mask symbol color to completely transparent. For the map items in the Print Composer, @map_id returns the Item ID. This Item ID can be customized in the map item properties as shown in Figure 10.5, on the next page. We use the SUBREGION values of the regions we want to highlight as the Item ID of the respective map item, for example, Central America in Figure 10.5, on the facing page.

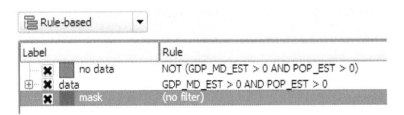

Figure 10.4: Add a rule for the mask

Figure 10.5: Customize the item id to control the masks

10.3   Finishing Touches

To finalize this map, we add labels for the title
as well as for some explanatory text. The final item we place is the legend which matches
the country colors to GDP values. To fit the
legend into the available space, we configure it
to use three columns. Figure 10.6, on the next
page shows the legend item settings. Make sure
to enable Split layers in the Columns section to
allow the Print Composer to split the legend
entries of a layer into multiple columns. Without this option, all legend entries of one layer
will be arranged in one column.

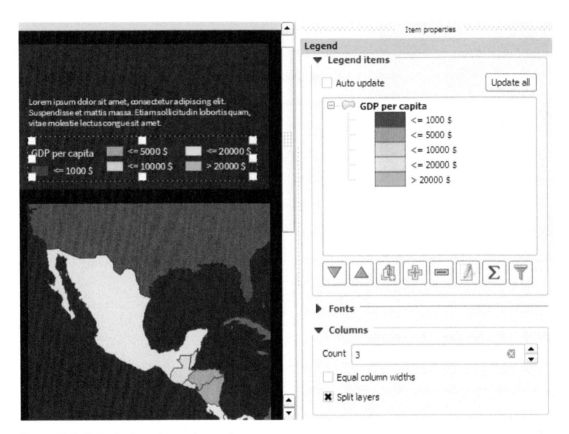

Figure 10.6: Split the legend into three columns

11. Conclusion

By flipping through the pages of this book it is possible to gain an understanding of the wide variety of mapping possibilities within QGIS. Additionally, we really hope you have worked through from scratch at least a few of the recipes, and ideally, most of them.

Gretchen Peterson often writes about how the act of creative learning is a two step process: seeing and doing. Our hope is that you've flipped through the book, seen what the capabilities of QGIS are, observed the general styling procedures, and then worked through the recipes.

If there are some recipes that you just don't have time to complete on your own, by all means make use of the completed project files (see http://locatepress.com/qmd_resources/) and take a close look at how they were done in a hands-on manner.

11.1 Share Your Maps!

If you've created a great map that you'd like to share, or if you'd like to peruse more map examples, consider joining and contributing to the QGIS Flickr group https://www.flickr.com/groups/qgis/. When you share your work, it's helpful to include an short explanation of the posted map and the QGIS version used to create it for those who might not be familiar with QGIS or with the map's subject matter.

The Flickr group shows what's possible, but obviously doesn't include detailed instructions. Looking through it does give you an idea of how this book covers only a selection of the many cartographic features available in QGIS.

11.2 Further Study

For even more map design material, we recommend the blogs of Nathan Woodrow, (e.g. "QGIS atlas on non geometry tables")[22] and Alexandre Neto, (e.g "Multiple format map se-

ries using QGIS 2.6 – Part 1")[23].

One option to continue improving your static map designs is to learn how to use graphic design software such as Inkscape. Exporting your designs from QGIS into Inkscape can allow for the application of custom filters and can greatly improve the process of labeling by hand, among other things, if those are important for your map.

One caution with the graphic design software approach, however, is that the map data loses its geographic context once its imported into one of these programs. This can cause problems if at some point you need to add additional geographic data to the map, it will be difficult to get it to align properly. While the use of graphic design software is something to explore, it isn't necessary to produce a beautiful map in QGIS as we've shown that many graphic design capabilities are now available within QGIS itself (e.g., layer and feature color blending).

Another natural next step is to use the styling techniques here to produce multi-scaled, interactive webmaps with QGIS. For starters, check out qgis2web and qgis2threejs. Anita Graser has given these two QGIS plugins a test run to create responsive webmap designs. You can see the results via a small concept page that presents cycle routes in 3D[24].

Qgis2web is the tool of choice to export classic slippy webmaps. This plugin makes it possible to generate Leaflet and OpenLayers3 maps from QGIS projects[25]. It provides access to different background maps and it's easy to replace them in the final HTML file in case you need something more exotic.

Qgis2threejs, on the other hand, creates 3D vi-

22. http://loc8.cc/qmd/woodrow
23. http://loc8.cc/qmd/neto
24. http://loc8.cc/qmd/3d_cycling
25. http://loc8.cc/qmd/qgis2web

Figure 11.1: 3D visualization example created with Qgis2threejs

sualizations based on three.js which uses WebGL. A showcase of Qgis2threejs, rendering OSM buildings, is available[26].

For general cartography study, Gretchen Peterson maintains a list of resources for learning cartography, fonts and icons, colors, web mapping, design, and creativity at http://gretchenpeterson.com/links.php .

26. http://loc8.cc/qmd/qgis2threejs

Index

Books from Locate Press

The PyQGIS Programmer's Guide - Extending QGIS just got easier! This book is your fast track to getting started with PyQGIS. After a brief introduction to Python, you'll learn how to understand the QGIS Application Programmer Interface (API), write scripts, and build a plugin. The book is designed to allow you to work through the examples as you go along. At the end of each chapter you'll find a set of exercises you can do to enhance your learning experience.

The PyQGIS Programmer's Guide is compatible with the version 2.0 API released with QGIS 2.x. All code samples and data are freely available from the book's website. Get started learning PyQGIS today!

Geospatial Power Tools - Everyone loves power tools. The GDAL and OGR utilities are the power tools of the GIS world, and best of all, they're free.

The utilities include tools for examining, converting, transforming, building and analysing data. This book is a collection of the GDAL and OGR documentation, but also includes substantial new content designed to help guide you in using the utilities to solve your current data problems.

Inside you'll find a quick reference for looking up the right syntax and example usage quickly. The book is divided into three parts: *Workflows and examples, GDAL raster utilities,* and *OGR vector utilities.* Once you get a taste of the power the GDAL/OGR suite provides, you'll wonder how you ever got along without them. This book will get you on the fast track to becoming more efficient in your GIS data processing efforts.

Books from Locate Press

The Geospatial Desktop provides a foundational level of knowledge for understanding GIS and the open source desktop mapping applications that are available for use, for free, today.

Learn about vector and raster data, how to convert data, interacting with spatial databases, creating new map data, geoprocessing, scripting, and more.

Special sections include focused learning on the Quantum GIS and GRASS GIS software platforms as well as an introduction to other packages.

The Geospatial Desktop is written by the founder of the Quantum GIS project, so you can rest assured that you will be led by one of the most knowledgeable authors on the subject.

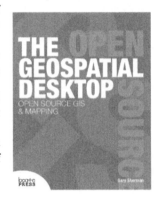

The Quantum GIS Training Manual - Get the jumpstart you need to learn this incredibly popular free desktop mapping and GIS toolset. Comprehensive and structured, your introduction begins with a quick download of example data, making it easy for you to work your way through the concepts and practical exercises, complete with answers and examples.

Ideal for classroom instruction and self-guided learning, included are all the materials needed to run a five day course on Quantum GIS, PostgreSQL and PostGIS. Content is structured for novice, intermediate and advanced users alike. Seasoned Quantum GIS users will also find tips and new techniques to apply to every mapping project. Windows, Mac OS X, or Linux? It's your choice, this book works for all.

Works with QGIS 1.8

Be sure to visit http://locatepress.com for information on new and upcoming titles.

Notes

CPSIA information can be obtained
at www.ICGtesting.com
Printed in the USA
BVOW10s0553090316
439644BV00023B/246/P